THE REPRESENTATIVE INHERITORS OF THE PROVINCIAL INTANGIBLE CULTURAL HERITAGE PROJECTS OF SHANDONG PROVINCE

山东省省级非物质文化遗产项目代表性传承人

第三卷

（Volume Ⅲ）

李国琳　主编

山东大学出版社

《山东省省级非物质文化遗产项目代表性传承人》
编辑委员会

Editorial Board of *The Representative Inheritors of the Provincial Intangible Cultural Heritage Projects of Shandong Province*

序

传承人是历史文化的重要承载者和传递者，他们身上承载着丰富知识、精湛技艺、实践经验等重要内容，是非物质文化遗产活态传承的重要组成部分，关乎每个项目是否能够长久流传于世。因此，保护、宣传、扶持传承人对于进一步做好非物质文化遗产（简称“非遗”）的保护工作具有重要意义。

山东是孔孟之乡、礼仪之邦，经过千百年的历史进程，形成了凝聚着齐鲁儿女勤劳与智慧的非物质文化遗产。近年来，全省各级文化主管部门认真贯彻中央和省委有关部署和要求，积极推动非遗的创造性转化和创新性发展，形成了非遗保护的“山东模式”，涌现了非遗名录山东现象、非遗传承山东路径、非遗培训山东探索、非遗利用山东实践等一大批具有浓郁山东特色的非遗保护传承做法和经验，整体工作走在全国前列。目前，山东省共有联合国教科文组织认定的“人类非遗代表作名录”项目8项、国家级代表性名录项目173项、省级代表性名录项目751项、市级代表性名录项目3490项、县级代表性名录项目10544项。现有国家级代表性传承人94名、省级代表性传承人447名、市级代表性传承人2312名、县级代表性传承人6717名。编撰《山东省省级非物质文化遗产项目代表性传承人》的目的，是希望通过此书，向民众介绍山东省国家级、省级传承人的基本情况、技艺特征、授徒传承等内容，展现山东省非遗传承人的精神风貌，增强民众对山东省传承人的了解，使得本书成果惠及大众，为社会共享。

非物质文化遗产是一个民族的生命记忆，体现着民族的智慧和精神。做好传承人的记录工作，就是在保护中华传统文化的基因，为中华文明接续薪火，也是为后人研究、宣传、利用非物质文化遗产提供宝贵资料。新时代，新担当，新作为，山东非遗保护工作将以习近平新时代中国特色社会主义思想为指导，不断推动全省非遗保护工作继续走在全国前列，为实现中华民族伟大复兴的中国梦而贡献更大的力量。

（山东省文化和旅游厅党组书记、厅长，山东省文物局局长　王磊）

PREFACE

Inheritors are important carriers and transmitters of history and culture. They have rich knowledge, exquisite skills and practical experience, etc. They are an important part of the active inheritance of intangible cultural heritage, and they are of vital importance to each project in terms of durability and propagation. Therefore, it is of great significance to protect, publicize and support the inheritors for the further protection of intangible cultural heritage.

Shandong Province is the hometown of Confucius and Mencius and the state of etiquette. After thousands of years of history, it has formed its intangible cultural heritage that embodies the diligence and wisdom of Qilu people. In recent years, the competent cultural authorities at all levels in Shandong Province have seriously implemented the relevant arrangements and requirements of the Central Committee and the Provincial Committee. They actively promoted the creative transformation and innovative development of intangible cultural heritage, and formed a "Shandong Model" of intangible cultural heritage protection. A large number of rich Shandong characteristics emerged, such as Shandong phenomenon of intangible cultural heritage list, Shandong path of intangible cultural heritage inheritance, Shandong exploration of intangible cultural heritage training, and Shandong practice of intangible cultural heritage utilization. The overall work is at the forefront of the country. At present, Shandong Province has 8 items in the "list of representative works of human intangible cultural heritage" recognized by UNESCO, 173 items in the national representative list, 751 items in the provincial representative list, 3,490 items in the municipal representative list and 10,544 items in the county-level representative list. There are 94 national, 447 provincial, 2,312 municipal and 6,717 county-level representative inheritors in Shandong Province. The purpose of compiling *The Representative Inheritors of The Provincial Intangible Cultural Heritage Projects of Shandong Province* is to introduce the basic information, technical characteristics, apprenticeship and other aspects of national and provincial inheritors to the public, show the spirit of Shandong Province's inheritors, and familiarize the public with Shandong Province's inheritors. We hope that the fruit of this book will benefit the public and be shared by the society.

Intangible cultural heritage is the life memory of a nation, which embodies the wisdom and spirit of the nation. Make a record of the work of inheritors is to protect the genes of Chinese traditional culture, to continue the Chinese civilization, and to provide valuable information for future generations to study, publicize and use intangible cultural heritage. A new era asks for new responsibilities and new actions. The protection of intangible cultural heritage in Shandong Province will be guided by Xi Jinping's Thought on Socialism with Chinese Characteristics for a New Era. We will continue to push the province's intangible cultural heritage protection work ahead of the rest of the country and make greater contributions to the realization of the Chinese dream of the great rejuvenation of the Chinese nation.

(Wang Lei, secretary of the party group and director of the Department of Culture and Tourism of Shandong Province, director of Shandong Provincial Bureau of Cultural Relics)

目 录 CONTENTS >>>

传统舞蹈
Traditional Dance

传统戏剧
Traditional Drama

曲 艺
Folk Art Forms

传统体育、游艺与杂技

Traditional Sports, Entertainment and Acrobatics

传统美术
Traditional Arts

传统技艺
Traditional Artistry

傳承人

传统舞蹈
Traditional Dance

小章竹马传承人——马镇华

马镇华，男，1939年出生，山东昌邑人。小章竹马第八代传承人。

跑竹马是昌邑市围子镇西小章村的一种传统民间歌舞。小章竹马表演的是元末明初时一位元朝武将奉命押送美女去南方进贡，遇山游山、遇水玩水的过程。表演队伍包括武术队、马队和18名扛腊杆的护马武术队员等。整个表演队伍最少60余人，多时100多人，阵容庞大，彩旗飘扬，十分壮观。竹马表演集出征列阵、戏剧表演、民间舞蹈和武术打斗于一体，程式复杂，花样繁多。

马镇华出生在小章竹马的故乡，他自小就被这种精彩的民间歌舞吸引。从记事起，马镇华便跟随小章竹马的第七代传承人马炳书进行学习。他几十年勤习不辍，熟练掌握了小章竹马的动作特点和技巧。除了擅长竹马表演，马镇华还负责竹马的制作、维修，演员的扮相、服装、唱腔训练、动作的编排以及武术队的分工，特别是马队串花跑场布阵时队形的变化，如“四门斗”“五花”“梅花瓣”“十字梅”“双沟”“二龙戏珠”“别杖子”“龙掉尾”等。

几十年来，马镇华多次带领小章竹马队伍积极参加各种文艺会演活动，使小章竹马的影响力不断扩大。2000~2005年，连续六年参演潍坊风筝节开幕式；2007~2010年，连续四年参加潍坊市非物质文化遗产展演活动。他们的演出曾多次登上报纸、电视等媒体，马镇华也被授予“昌邑市先进文化工作者”“潍坊市百名文化名人”荣誉称号。

然而，目前小章竹马濒临灭绝，竹马的扎制技艺也面临失传。小章竹马的演员们大多年事已高，有的已经谢世，演员后继乏人。已近耄耋之年的马镇华多年来一直自费维修竹马、服装道具等，努力传承着小章竹马，为这一古老民间歌舞的发展做出了重要贡献。

Ma Zhenhua—Inheritor of Xiaozhang Bamboo Horse Dance

Ma Zhenhua, male, was born in 1939 in Changyi, Shandong Province. He is the eighth-generation inheritor of Xiaozhang bamboo horse dance.

Xiaozhang bamboo horse dance is a traditional folk dance of West Xiaozhang Village, Weizi Town, Changyi, Shandong Province. The dance depicts a group of horsemen led by a military commander appointed by the government in the late stages of the Yuan Dynasty. They enjoyed the beautiful landscape along the way when escorting beauties down to the South as tributes. The spectacular performance combines battle array, drama, folk dance, and martial arts. Generally, there are more than 60 to more than 100 performers including martial arts team, horsemen team and 18 martial arts performers carrying waxed bamboo poles to guard horses.

When he was a little boy, Ma Zhenhua was deeply attracted by the dance and learnt it under the guidance of Ma Bingshu, the seventh-generation inheritor of Xiaozhang bamboo horse dance. Mr. Ma has been working hard for decades and has entirely mastered the dance moves and other skills. Mr. Ma also makes and repairs bamboo horses, provides dancers' look, costumes and singing training, designs new dance movements, and arrays the roles of the martial arts performers. He pays meticulous attention to the changes from one battle array to another one. Those battle arrays are named "Four Directions Doors (riding in a quadrilateral)" "Five Flowers (riding to make the shape of a plum blossom)" "Shizi Plums (riding to the diagonally opposite corner)" "Shuanggou (riding to the diagonally opposite corner and then riding around the center of the circle for several times)" "Two Dragons Playing a Burning Ball (three teams of horsemen riding in three lines)" "Biezhangzi (riding in a quadrilateral and then riding backwards)" and "Longdiaowei (reining in in front of the dragon flag)".

Over the last several decades, Ma Zhenhua has brought Xiaozhang bamboo borse dance onto the stage with other dancers, thus having enhanced its reputation. Their performance was staged at the opening ceremony of the Weifang Kite Festival for six consecutive years (from 2000 to 2005) and at the Weifang's Intangible Cultural Heritage of Humanity Exhibition for four consecutive years (from 2007 and 2010), and also appeared in newspapers and on television for many times.

However, Xiaozhang bamboo horse dance and the bamboo horsing-making techniques are going to disappear. The dancers are growing old and some have passed away. Ma Zhenhua, who is in his eighties, has been repairing bamboo horses, costumes and props at his own expense for many years, and working hard to hand down the dance to the younger generation. Having made a significant contribution to the development of Xiaozhang bamboo horse dance, Mr. Ma has won the title of "Excellent Promoter of Arts and Culture in Changyi" and ranked as the "Top 100 Cultural Figure in Weifang".

地秧歌传承人——王兆章

王兆章，男，1938年出生，山东高密人。

高密地秧歌又称“地蹅”“秧歌耍”“秧歌戏”“扮秧歌”等，流传于高密、昌邑县境内。它起源于当地的祭祀活动，由于在当地很受欢迎，后逐渐由祭祀扩展到春节、元宵节等欢庆活动中。高密地秧歌是一种别具特色的传统舞蹈，除了简单地扭秧歌，还有丰富的表演形式和剧目内容。地秧歌的角色有秧歌头、老旦、鼓子、棒槌、腊花、小嫚等，一般都是男扮女装。它的音乐形式以民歌小调为主，有时也唱老腔、小腔、秧歌头调等。舞中有唱、唱中有戏、戏中有舞的地秧歌是当地群众喜闻乐见的娱乐活动。

王兆章出生于民间文艺之家，他的祖父、父亲都是当时民间文艺活动的骨干，受到父辈的熏陶和培养，王兆章十分热爱民间文艺工作。1979年，在公社文化站工作期间，王兆章更加清楚地认识到地秧歌的价值，于是正式拜王家寺村王延升等3位民间老艺人为师，学习高密地秧歌。由于聪明好学、刻苦勤奋，王兆章很快就学会了地秧歌的演、唱、编排等技艺。他在地蹅上扭、跑、跳、说、唱都灵活自如，又扭又唱，别有一番风趣。

在上级文化部门的支持下，王兆章等人努力挖掘、抢救、编排高密地秧歌。同时，王兆章还致力于高密地秧歌的传承。他帮助其他村排练演出地秧歌，并取得了成功。2006年，王兆章还将地秧歌教授给十几名演员。2010年，为迎接红高粱艺术节，王兆章等人在夏庄镇刘家村进行的秧歌排演，在保持原有风格的同时，扩大了演出队伍，增强了表演效果，使这一舞蹈形式更加适合节日氛围。多年来，王兆章一直为高密地秧歌的传承与发展做着不懈的努力。

Wang Zhaozhang—Inheritor of Gaomi Yangko

Wang Zhaozhang, male, was born in 1938 in Gaomi, Shandong Province.

Gaomi yangko (also known as Gaomi yangge, yangko drama or yangko opera) is a traditional folk dance developing from the sacrificial practices in Gaomi and Changyi, Weifang, Shandong Province, which was later also performed during the Spring Festival and Lantern Festival owning to its popularity among the locals. The dance combines yangko, dance, drama, and music. Gaomi yangko features six main role types, yangko leader, laodan, drummer, wooden club player, lahua and xiaoman. The dancers are normally males dressing as females. The dance is accompanied by folk tunes, sometimes by laoqiang, xiaoqiang, or yangko melodies.

Wang Zhaozhang was born in a family of folk arts and culture lovers in Gaomi. Mr. Wang's grandfather and father were then working to promote folk arts and culture. Having been influenced profoundly by and learnt from his grandfather and father, he also fell in love with folk arts and culture. When working in the cultural station of the people's commune in 1979, Mr. Wang recognized the value of Gaomi yangko, so he started to learn the dance from three elder folk artists (one of them is named Wang Yansheng) in Wangjiasi Village, Jiangzhuang Town, Gaomi. Mr. Wang learnt how to dance, sing, and design new dance movements and quickly mastered Gaomi yankgo through practice and effort. When performing, he wriggles, runs, jumps, narrates and sings, having enjoyed himself immensely.

Supported by the local cultural department, Wang Zhaozhang spares no effort to excavate and preserve the legacy of Gaomi yangko, and design new dance routines with other folk arts and culture lovers. He succeeded in instructing other villages to rehearse Gaomi yangko and give performances. In 2006, Mr. Wang taught the dance to a dozen of actors. In 2010, Mr. Wang and other folk arts and culture lovers rehearsed Gaomi yankgo in Liujia Village, Xiazhuang Town, Gaomi, for the Red Sorghum Art Festival. There were more dancers, which made the performance more appealing and created a more festive atmosphere. For years, Mr. Wang has devoted his life to the development and promotion of Gaomi yangko and made substantial contributions.

闹海传承人——黄冠群

黄冠群，女，1960 年出生，山东寿光人。现为寿光市舞蹈家协会主席。

闹海是流传于寿光市境内一种较为古老的民间舞蹈。表演者的角色分为“海仙”“众仙”“舞云者”“丑婆”，表演时需要在头部或上身装扮根据海洋动物如鱼、虾、蟹、蚌、蛙等形象扎制而成的道具，表演者男女相间，表演人数不等，少则十几人，多则百余人。表演形式以跑场为主线，队形有“辫子花”“里梅花”“正反推磨”等十几种。闹海的表演手法夸张、浪漫，既粗犷又细腻，闹中有序、序中有活、活中不乱、乱中有规，千姿百态，栩栩如生。表演时用打击乐和吹奏乐伴奏，乐曲则以秧歌调为主。

黄冠群是闹海舞蹈的第五代传承人，她具有演、编、导的基本功底。从事群众文化工作 30 多年来，黄冠群一直致力于闹海这一民间舞蹈的挖掘、整理与编排。她多次拜访擅长闹海舞蹈的老艺人，不断查阅民间闹海舞蹈的相关知识，深入研究闹海的鼓曲与舞蹈动作。黄冠群结合自身集舞、戏、曲艺术特长于一身的特点，挖掘闹海编演历史和不同时代的演出背景，重新编排《闹海》。她非常注重舞蹈演员的形体与道具之间的和谐统一，悉心指导演员将鱼、龟、虾、蟹等形象特征运用到角色表演中，以达到人物形态与道具造型以及队形变化完美结合的效果。由她编排、指导、演练的《闹海》先后参加了第九届和第十三届潍坊国际风筝会开幕式，连续三届参加了中国寿光蔬菜科技博览会艺术节民俗表演，每次都有精彩的亮点展现给观众，深受观众好评。

1990 年，黄冠群重新编排的《闹海》被编入《中国民族民间舞蹈集成·山东卷》；2005 年,《闹海》被编入《齐鲁特色文化丛书》。黄冠群为《闹海》这一优秀民间传统舞蹈的传承与发展做出了重要贡献。

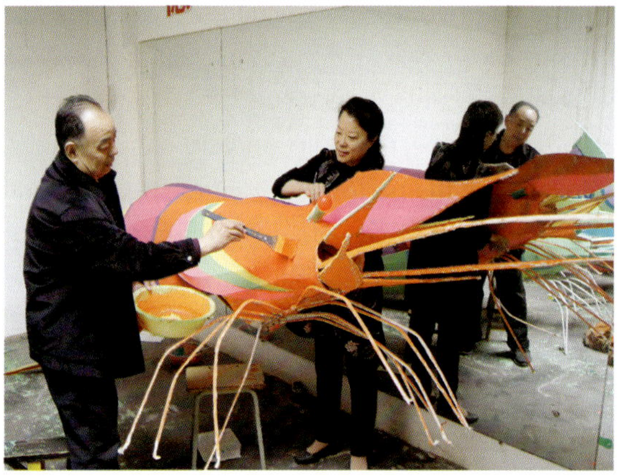

Huang Guanqun—Inheritor of Naohai Dance

Huang Guanqun, female, was born in 1960 in Shouguang City, Shandong Province. She is the chairman of Shouguang Dancer Association.

Naohai dance is a traditional folk dance in Shouguang City, Shandong Province, China, featuring a bold, exquisite, romantic and vivid performance. There are a dozen to over 100 dancers (50/50, for men and women) playing the roles of gods in the sea or heaven, cloud wavers, or women clowns. When performing, dancers wear props made in the shape of marine animals such as clam, crab, fish, frog and shrimp. Dancers run in a dozen of formations, such like "Bianzihua" "Limeihua" and "Zhengfantuimo". The dance is accompanied by percussion and wind music, featuring a Yangko melody.

Huang Guanqun is the fifth-generation inheritor of Naohai dance. Not only can she perform the dance, she can design and direct new dance movements. Ms. Huang has been working to discover more about Naohai dance and design new dance movements when serving as a promoter of Chinese folk arts and culture for over 30 years. Ms. Huang kept visiting many elder dancers good at the dance, consulting the relevant information about the dance, and studying the drum music and dance movements. Taking its different historical settings into consideration, she reestablished the movements of Naohai dance. Ms. Huang instructs the dancers how to perform like marine animals when wearing the props, and emphasizes the harmony between actors, props and formations. Ms. Huang has brought the new Naohai dance to the opening ceremonies of the 9th and 13th Weifang International Kite Festival and to the China (Shouguang) International Vegetable Sci-Tech Fair for three consecutive years, which have won loud applause.

In 1990, the new Naohai dance was compiled into *Chinese Traditional Folk Dances Shandong*. In 2005, it was compiled into *Folk Arts and Culture Collection of Shandong*. Huang Guanqun has made enormous contributions to the development and promotion of Naohai dance.

三皇舞传承人——魏凤莲

魏凤莲，女，1947 年出生，山东鄄城人，三皇舞第十八代传承人。

三皇舞是流传于山东菏泽一带的传统民间舞蹈，三皇即天皇、地皇、人皇，是先民心中的领袖和精神偶像。三皇舞是一种集体舞，一般以 16~20 人为宜（男女各半）。女穿彩衣，腰系彩带；男披兽皮或树叶形舞衣，头戴柳条圈或彩带，手持牛胛骨。表演时，男女分为两组列队出场，在乐队伴奏下，模仿猿人爬行、站立、行走、蹦跳、狩猎、农作、祭祀等动作。三皇舞队形简单多变，有"横排""直行"“八卦图”“二龙吐须”等。该舞的主要特点是屈腿佝偻而舞，这是模仿原始人的典型动作，也是与其他舞蹈的区别之处。

魏凤莲从学校毕业后，在家务农，利用农闲时间学习三皇舞。1971 年，魏凤莲师从三皇舞第十七代传承人陈凤娥，进行系统学习与研究。由于聪明伶俐、刻苦勤奋，加上老师的严格指导和悉心传授，魏凤莲很快掌握了三皇舞的主要动作和表演技巧。

三皇舞所用吹弹及打击乐器比较单纯，乐曲古朴不尚华丽。魏凤莲表演的爬、跳、蹲、走等动作粗犷豪放，与乐曲巧妙合一，将人们对天地的崇拜、敬重之情，对祖先的缅怀之情，丰收时的喜悦之情展现得淋漓尽致。四十几年来，魏凤莲多次带队参加省、市、县级文艺展演活动，精彩的表演深得广大观众的喜爱和欢迎。

为了更好地传承与发展三皇舞，魏凤莲举办了三皇舞培训班，言传身教，培养了几十名学员，使三皇舞这一古老的民间艺术后继有人。2007 年，魏凤莲参加菏泽牡丹花会广场文艺展演，荣获二等奖。

Wei Fenglian—Inheritor of Three Emperors Dance

Wei Fenglian, was born in 1947 in Juancheng County, Heze City, Shandong Province. Ms. Wei is the eighteenth-generation inheritor of three emperors dance.

Three emperors dance is a traditional folk dance of Heze City, Shandong Province, China. "Three emperors" refers to Emperor of Heaven, Emperor of Earth and Emperor of Human, who are the leaders and spiritual icons of the ancients. Generally, there are 16 to 20 dancers (50/50, for men and women). Male dancers wear animal skins or leaf-shaped clothing with wicker wreathes or ribbons on their heads, holding the scapula of cattle; female dancers wear colorful clothing with ribbons around their waists. When performing, dancers are divided into two groups by gender. They crawl, stand, walk, jump, hunt, farm, and do sacrificial practices like ape men. Three emperors dance has many simple formations, such as "Horizontal Line" "Vertical Line""Bagua" and "Two Dragons Spiting Their Whiskers".

Wei Fenglian became a farmer and learnt three emperors dance in the leisure time after graduation. In 1971, Ms. Wei started to learn and study the dance under the guidance of Chen Fenge, the seventeenth-generation inheritor of three emperors dance. Ms. Wei quickly mastered the dance movements and techniques through practice and effort.

When performing, dancers are accompanied by simple percussion and wind instruments. During the performance, Wei Fenglian crawls, walks, squats, and jumps like an ape woman, going perfectly with the music. Her performance reflects worship to heaven, earth and ancestors and joy with good harvests. Over the last 40 years, Ms. Wei has staged three emperors dance in various events at the provincial, municipal and county levels with other dancers, which has been well-liked by the public.

Wei Fenglian offers three emperors dance training class and has taught the dance to dozens of students, with an aim to better develop and promote the dance. In 2007, Ms. Wei performed at Heze Peony Exhibition and won the second prize.

陈官短穗花鼓传承人——张兰青

张兰青，女，1971 年出生，山东广饶人。陈官短穗花鼓第三代传承人。

陈官短穗花鼓流传于广饶县的陈官乡。它原是旧社会流浪艺人借以乞讨谋生的手段，后逐渐形成技艺独特的民间舞蹈。它的独特之处在于用以打鼓的不是鼓槌，而是系在鼓槌一端的鼓穗。鼓槌长 10 厘米，系有 60 厘米长的短鞭，鞭头经手工加工成疙瘩穗，即“鼓穗”，穗长 60 厘米，用于击鼓。通常花鼓在腰间是活动的，这就要求鼓者掌握熟练高超的打鼓技艺，“打场脚微颠，八字腿弓箭，击打头略晃，跑鼓轻如仙”就形象地写出了具体的动作要求。

张兰青出身于短穗花鼓世家，她的父亲及叔父都是陈冠短穗花鼓传承人。张兰青自幼跟随父亲、叔父学习短穗花鼓技艺，掌握了表演的精华和完整的动作步骤。为了更好地传承与发展陈官短穗花鼓，张兰青及其团队对短穗花鼓的表演形式做了改进，他们将原来一人打镲说唱、一人击鼓表演的传统改为一人唱或两人对唱，多人用镲、锣、钹、唢呐和打鼓等乐器伴奏，数人乃至几十人集体表演。这一突破使陈官短穗花鼓更加适应大型演出，也更能营造节日的欢庆气氛。

张兰青多次带队参加各种市、乡艺术表演，并在历次演出中都取得了较好的成绩。1986 年，张兰青的短穗花鼓表演在《中国民族民间舞蹈集成》中获得一等奖；2008 年，张兰青参演的陈官短穗花鼓在东营市民间艺术会演中获得一等奖。为了培养后辈人才、振兴陈官短穗花鼓，张兰青积极组织短穗花鼓队伍成员的培训与练习，同时，还将短穗花鼓技艺引进校园，在陈官乡中心小学成立了名为“快乐敲击吧”的培训基地，开展陈官短穗花鼓的普及性教育，培养了一批由小学生组成的少儿花鼓队，为这一古老民间舞蹈的传承做出了贡献。

Zhang Lanqing—Inheritor of Chenguan Short-Tassel Flower Drum Dance

Zhang Lanqing, female, was born in 1971, into a family of inheritors of Chenguan short-tassel flower drum dance in Guangrao County, Dongying City, Shandong Province. Ms. Zhang is the third-generation inheritor of Chengguan short-tassel flower drum dance.

Chenguan short-tassel flower drum dance is a popular folk dance in Chenguan Township, Guangrao County, Dongying City, Shandong Province. The dance originated from the means of livelihood of vagrants in the old days. Dancers wear removable waist drums and use the drum tassels, instead of drumsticks, to beat the drums. The drumstick is about 10 centimeters long with a 60-centimeter short whip. One end of the whip is tied into a knot, which is the drum tassel. When performing, excellent dancers do small dance steps, turn their feet outward, slightly nod their heads, and dance as light as a feather.

Both Zhang Lanqing's father and uncle are inheritors of Chenguan short-tassel flower drum dance. When she was a little girl, Ms. Zhang started to learn the dance from her father and uncle and completely mastered the dance movements. In the past, there were only two performers. One narrated and sang when clashing small cymbals, while the other beat the drum. Ms. Zhang has improved the performance with her team to better promote Chenguan short-tassel flower drum dance. When performing, there are several to dozens of performers. One performer sing (or two performers sing to each other), while other performers play cymbals, drums, gongs, or suonas. The breakthrough makes the dance more suitable for large-scale performance and makes it possible to create a more festive atmosphere.

Zhang Lanqing has performed Chenguan short-tassel flower drum dance in various competitions in towns and cities, and has given excellent performance. In 1986, Ms. Zhang's performance of Chenguan short-tassel flower drum dance won the first prize in "The Collection of Chinese Traditional Folk Dances". In 2008, she performed the dance with others in the Dongying Folk Arts and Culture Show and won the first prize. Ms. Zhang has been working to develop and promote Chenguan short-tassel flower drum dance. Ms. Zhang offers training for the dancers, and introduces the dance to pupils. She has built a training center in Chenguan Township Central Elementary School and set up a flower drum dance team consisting of pupils. She has made important contributions to the development and promotion of the dance.

阴阳板传承人——王长军

王长军，男，1965 年出生，山东邹城人。

阴阳板是一种两板相击而舞的民间舞蹈。所谓阴阳板，是指一长一短两块柳木板，板上刻有吉祥图纹，板尾钻孔，用皮条相连，板头配有小铃铛，舞动起来叮当作响。阴阳板表演队伍少则百人，多则上千，队伍前面是一把黄罗伞，其后是椭圆形黄扇，随之便是由黑虎旗带领的旗队，旗队后是锣鼓队，锣鼓队后即是阴阳板舞队。

1978 年，王长军考入邹城市豫剧团，担任演员，这为他以后学习、表演阴阳板奠定了基础。自 1980 年开始，他跟随杨成举学习阴阳板，之后多次参加阴阳板排练演出活动，获得专家和群众的一致好评。

现代阴阳板表演摒弃了一些祭祀活动，主要保留了舞蹈内容。在进行表演时，王长军赤胸，身披“八卦带”，下着灯笼裤，双手持板，不停地打击和搓击，发出两种不同的声音，即“阴阳声”。他挥板在身体前后左右上下打击，行动敏捷，并与队友合作瞬间变化出“双环阵”“双扣花”“降祥云”“龙展目”等各种队形，令人叫绝。王长军的阴阳板动作憨厚大方，粗犷奔放，又不乏细腻灵活，极富观赏性。

王长军多次带领阴阳板表演队伍参加农民文化艺术节和社会公益活动演出，积极推广阴阳板这一民间传统舞蹈。2009 年，其表演的阴阳板专题片在中央电视台四套播出。2010 年 9 月，王长军参加中国曲阜国际孔子文化艺术节开幕式，演出阴阳板。演出之余，王长军时刻不忘阴阳板的传承。近年来，他在邹城市后八里村专门成立阴阳板传承基地，培养了 40 余名阴阳板传承人，为阴阳板这一古老艺术注入了新的活力。

Wang Changjun—
Inheritor of Yin and Yang Clappers Dance

Wang Changjun, male, was born in 1965 in Zoucheng County, Weifang City, Shandong Province.

Yin and yang clappers dance is a traditional folk dance. The yin and yang clappers consist of two willow planks, with one longer than the other one. The clappers are engraved with auspicious patterns, and bound together by a leather strap through the hole made at one end of the planks. The other end of the clappers is equipped with little bells, which clang during the performance. Generally, a performance needs more than a hundred and even a thousand dancers. When performing, the dance group is led by a dancer holding a yellow canopy, followed by a dancer holding an elliptical yellow fan. Then come flag wavers led by a black tiger flag, followed by gong players and drummers. Yin and yang clappers dance are at the end.

In 1978, Wang Changjun started to work at the Zoucheng Yu Opera Troupe as an actor and improved his technique there. In 1980, Mr. Wang started to learn yin and yang clappers dance under the guidance of Yang Chengju. Since then, he has performed the dance with other dancers for many times and is well liked by experts and the audience.

The modern yin and yang clappers dance does not include sacrificial practices in the old days. When performing, Wang Changjun wears a Bagua strip and knickerbockers. Mr. Wang makes two different sounds representing yin and yang with the clappers. He swings his arm, clashes the clappers and moves agilely with other dancers to perform different formations such as "Shuanghuan-zhen" "Shuangkouhua", "Jiangxiangyun", and "Longzhanmu". Mr. Wang's performance is bold, exquisite, vivid, and very appealing to the audience.

Wang Changjun performs yin and yang clappers dance during the Folk Arts and Culture Festival and social welfare activities with other dances to promote the dance. In 2009, a documentary on yin and yang clappers dance appeared on China Central Television-4. In September 2010, Mr. Wang performed the dance at the opening ceremony of China (Qufu) International Confucius Cultural and Art Festival. He has been working to promote Yin and Yang Clappers Dance. Over the years, Mr. Wang has built a yin and yang clapper dance center in Houbali Village in Zoucheng, and taught the dance to 40 people, thus injecting into the dance fresh vitality.

火虎传承人——周长来

周长来，男，1955年出生，山东邹城人，火虎第四代传承人。

火虎是邹城市平阳寺人民在长期的农耕劳作生活中形成的别具特色的舞蹈表演，具有气势宏大、观赏性强等特点，距今已有200余年的历史。火虎表演是综合民间舞狮和民间礼花筋表演结合而成，初期礼花筋数量少、易点燃、易操作，现在礼花筋已达2000余根，逐渐演变到整个“虎身”。火虎表演的时间多是每年农历二月初二或其他节日的晚上。在傍晚时分，一般先是高跷、二仙斗、舞龙灯等其他民间艺术进行表演，待天黑以后，火虎表演才隆重登场，使表演现场的气氛达到高潮。

周长来出生于火虎表演世家，其爷爷、父亲均是火虎表演的高手。受家庭影响，周长来自幼喜爱火虎表演。1984年，其跟随父亲正式学习火虎表演，研究火虎舞的表演技巧，将舞蹈中体现出的不畏强暴、勇斗猛兽的英雄主义精神进行传承和创新。

火虎表演具有鲁南一带浓厚的地方特色，周长来在继承传统特色的基础上，将“打虎”这一古老的英雄主义主题加以现代演绎，还在传统舞狮表演的基础上加以改革创新。创新后的火虎表演展示了邹城一带浓郁的历史文化气韵，生动、形象地再现了古老的打虎故事，将人们带回到历史的情境之中。周长来还将舞蹈动作和武术动作融合在一起，使得火虎表演起来动作刚劲有力、威猛大方而又不乏美观。

从学习火虎表演至今，每逢春节及其他重大节日，周长来都会在邹城市境内进行火虎表演。他曾多次参加市、县级民间艺术表演比赛并获奖。由周长来参演的火虎表演还被制成《火虎火起来》特别节目，亮相中央电视台新闻频道。目前，周长来已将火虎表演技艺传授给了下一代，使这一古老的民间艺术得到了传承与保护。

Zhou Changlai—Inheritor of Sparking Tiger Dance

Zhou Changlai, male, was born in 1955 in Zoucheng County, Weifang City, Shandong Province. Mr. Zhou is the fourth-generation inheritor of sparking tiger dance.

Sparking tiger dance is a traditional folk dance combining lion dance and fireworks show, created by the locals in Pingyang Temple Town, Zoucheng County, Jining City, Shandong Province during farming seasons, boasting a history of more than 200 years. Dance performers used to carry a small amount of fireworks, which were easy to light. Now they have to carry more than 2,000 fireworks on their head and back. Generally, the performance is given on the evening of the second day of the second lunar month or the evenings of other festivals. On the early evening of that day, folk shows such as stilt walking, erxiandou, and dragon lantern dance are performed first. Sparking Tiger Dance is performed after dark, bringing the performance to a climax.

Zhou Changlai's grandfather and father are both sparking tiger dance performers. Influenced by them, Mr. Zhou was deeply attracted by the dance when he was a little boy. In 1984, he started to learn sparking tiger dance under the guidance of his father. Aside from studying and inheriting the technique of the dance, he has added new elements to the heroism displayed by the dance.

Sparking tiger dance has local characteristics in the south part of Shandong Province. Zhou Changlai's performance displays the heroism of fighting a tiger in a modern way. The new sparking tiger dance represents the cultural and historical flavor of Zoucheng County and vividly reproduces the old story of fighting atiger. Mr. Zhou has added martial arts to the dance, combining hardness and softness.

Zhou Changlai performs sparking tiger dance in Zoucheng during the Spring Festival and other major festivals. Mr. Zhou has taken part in many competitions at the municipal or county levels and won many prizes. His performance with other dancers has been shot and appeared on as a special show promoting sparking tiger dance on China Central Television—News Channel. Mr. Zhou has taught the dance to the younger generation to better develop and promote the dance.

蹉地舞传承人——黄象浩

黄象浩，男，1955年出生，山东莱芜人。蹉地舞第三代传承人，“莱芜市十大民间艺术之星”。

蹉地舞是流传在莱城区和庄乡一带的一种古老的民间祭祀舞蹈，它起源于清乾隆年间的原山庙会，距今已有200余年的历史。蹉地舞简单易学，富有特色，主要动作有“单脚蹉”“双脚蹉”“交叉蹉”“蹦跳蹉”等。跳蹉地舞时强调身体前倾，两臂自然摇摆，突出一个“蹉”字，其要点是“上身向前倾，双脚往后蹬，一步半个蹉，似把原山蹬”，保留着登山动作的基本形态和韵味。蹉地舞以生动、欢快的情绪为基调，以轻快的节奏、活泼的乐曲来反映百姓的喜悦心情，其队形变化保持着“直线不弯曲，队伍不相离”的艺术特点。

黄象浩对本村的蹉地舞艺术耳濡目染，在莱城区和庄乡文体广播站任站长期间，他更加清楚地认识到蹉地舞的文化价值。为了更好地传承蹉地舞表演艺术，他拜本村蹉地舞第一代传承人郭文焕、郭庆功两位老艺人为师，熟练掌握了蹉地舞的基本动作、步伐和具体跳法。另外，黄象浩还着力于蹉地舞的发掘和编排，为蹉地舞的传承和发展做出了突出贡献。

黄象浩积极参加各种文化活动并获得多项殊荣。1989年1月，他参与了艺术科学国家重点研究项目“中国民间文学三套集成”的编纂工作，被省文化厅、省民委、省文联评为先进工作者。2000年9月，他编排的民间舞蹈《蹉地舞》在莱城区农民文化艺术节中荣获表演二等奖和优秀节目创作奖。2003年6月，他编写的《山东民间舞蹈<蹉地舞>及舞曲是怎样产生的》一文获得“山东省文化艺术科学优秀成果三等奖”。为使这一优秀文化遗产得到传承，从20世纪90年代初期至今，黄象浩一直在本乡举办蹉地舞培训班，组织辅导农村民间艺术表演人员百余人，目前已培养出蹉地舞第四、第五代传人。

Huang Xianghao—Inheritor of Cuodi Dance

Huang Xianghao, male, was born in 1955 in Laiwu, Shandong Province. Mr. Huang is the third-generation inheritor of Cuodi dance and a top ten folk artist of Laiwu City.

Cuodi dance is a traditional folk dance for sacrificial practices in Hezhuang Township, Laicheng District, Jinan City, Shandong Province. The dance comes from the Yuanshan Temple Fair during the reign of Emperor Qianlong of the Qing dynasty, boasting a history of more than 200 years. It features fast rhythm and sweet and perky melody, reflecting the sense of joy of the locals. When performing, dancers lean forward and do single-, double-, cross-over leg hops and jumps, with two arms swinging naturally. It is important for the dancers to lean their upper body forward while stepping backwards, just like climbing a mountain. The dancers always perform in a straight line.

Huang Xianghao was deeply attracted by Cuodi dance. When working as the head of the Culture and Sports Broadcasting Station in Hezhuang Township, he recognized the cultural value of the dance. Mr. Huang learnt Cuodi dance from Guo Wenhuan and Guo Qinggong, two first-generation inheritors of Cuodi dance, and mastered the dance movements, routines and steps. Mr. Huang has been working to discover more about Cuodi dance and design new dance routines, making huge contributions to the development and promotion of the dance.

Huang Xianghao has participated in various cultural activities and won many awards. In January 1989, he was engaged in the writing of *Three Collections of Folk Literature*, a national key research project on arts, and won the award for "Excellent Promoter of Arts and Culture" by the Department of Culture, the Ethnic and Religious Affairs Committee, and the Literature and Art Association of Shandong Province. In September 2000, Cuodi dance under the guidance of Mr. Huang won the second prize and the award for excellent performance in the Folk Arts and Culture Festival in Laicheng District. In June 2003, his essay "The History and Development of Cuodi Dance" won the third prize of Culture and Arts Outstanding Work in Shandong Province.

Huang Xianghao has offered Cuodi dance training class in Hezhuang Township and taught the dance to over 100 dancers. Now the dance has its fourth- and fifth-generation inheritors.

猴呱哒鞭传承人——张学法

张学法，男，出生于 1929 年，山东苍山人。

猴呱哒鞭也叫“双鞭落子”，起源于临沂兰陵西横沟崖村，至今有 100 多年的历史。它的表演内容以男性打花鞭模拟猴的形态舞姿与手握竹板和撒拉机的伴舞者（女性）穿插逗乐为主，主要特征是节奏明快、动作性强、气氛热烈。尤其是男性持鞭模仿猴的形态，穿插“单鞭戏落子”“双鞭戏落子”“对打花鞭”等动作，形成了舞、戏、歌相融汇的艺术风格，富有鲁西南特有的乡土气息。

张学法受家庭熏陶，自幼热爱猴呱哒鞭舞，14 岁就跟随外祖父学习。经过刻苦勤奋的练习，张学法持鞭模仿的猴的形态惟妙惟肖，身不离鞭、鞭不离身，腾挪闪跃，深受群众喜爱。多年来，张学法一直为猴呱哒鞭舞的传承与发展做着大量工作。20 世纪 60~80 年代，张学法培育了数名猴呱哒鞭舞的传承人，使猴呱哒鞭舞这一传统民间舞蹈后继有人。

由张学法带队的猴呱哒鞭舞表演曾多次荣获各种奖项。1983 年，张学法参演的猴呱哒鞭舞被编入《中国民族民间舞蹈集成·山东卷》一书；2001 年，苍山县文化局聘请张学法重新挖掘传授猴呱哒鞭舞，张学法新颖的表演受到了观众的喜爱；2007 年，张学法组织了 60 多人的猴呱哒鞭舞艺术队，在苍山首届民间秧歌会表演中荣获一等奖，在临沂市第七届秧歌会表演中荣获金奖。由张学法带领的苍山兰陵猴呱哒鞭舞舞蹈组还曾进京献艺，登上了中央电视台 3 套《民歌中国》的舞台。在张学法等人的努力下，猴呱哒鞭舞这一特有的民间舞蹈形式在发源地兰陵镇以及苍山县广大农村得以流传，发展成为苍山乃至沂蒙山区乐舞文化的重要组成部分。

Zhang Xuefa—Inheritor of Houguada Whip Dance

Zhang Xuefa, male, was born in 1929 in Cangshan County, Linyi City, Shandong Province.

Houguada whip dance, or two whips dance, is a folk dance created in West Henggouya Village, Lanling County, Linyi City, Shandong Province, boasting a history of more than 100 years. The performance combines dance, drama and song. The dance features fast rhythm, powerful movement and carnival atmosphere.

When performing, there are male dancers imitating the movements of monkeys by waving whips and female dancers telling stories with bamboo clappers and saliji (both are musical instruments). The male dancers hold the whip to imitate the monkeys, interspersed with "single whip play" "double whip play" and "swinging whip" and other action combinations.

Zhang Xuefa was deeply attracted by houguada wipe dance when he was a little boy. Mr. Zhang started to learn the dance under the guidance of his grandfather at the age of 14. He mastered the dance movements through practice and effort. When performing, Mr. Zhang behaves just like a money, and he waves his whips consummately. His performance gains popularity among the locals. Over the years, Mr. Zhang has been working to develop and promote houguada whip dance. During the 1960s to the 1980s, he taught the dance to several people, who became new inheritors of the dance.

The houguada whip dance performance led by Zhang Xuefa has won numerous awards. In 1983, Mr. Zhang's dance was compiled into *Collection of Chinese Traditional Folk Dances: Shandong*. In 2001, he was invited by Bureau for Culture of Lanling County to teach houguada whip dance. In 2007, Mr. Zhang set up a houguada whip dance team with over 60 dancers. The team won the first prize in the first Folk Yangko Festival in Lanling County and a gold medal in the seventh Yangko Show in Linyi. The team led by Zhang Xuefa went to Beijing to perform the dance and appeared on the China Folk Song Show on China Central Television Channel 3.

Though the efforts of Zhang Xuefa and others, houguada whip dance has been popular in Cangshan County and became an important part of the folk music and dance culture of Cangshan and Yimeng Mountain regions.

柳林降狮舞传承人——杨乃让

杨乃让，男，1963年出生，山东冠县人，柳林降狮舞第九代传承人。

冠县柳林镇，隶属于聊城市，位于冀鲁豫三省交界处。冠县柳林降狮舞是清朝初年从堂邑（今东昌府区堂邑镇）县城传到此地的，迄今已有300多年的历史。降狮舞表现的是一位“耍狮人”为了替民除害，手持灵芝草、倒心钩和八卦阴阳旗，追踪、查找、相斗，最后降服一对狮子的故事。各种舞蹈动作均沿着这条情节线进行表演，有“踩鼓”“查蹄印”“轰狮子”“撒旗子”和“踩四门”等。这些舞蹈动作在雄壮、宏大的锣鼓伴奏中完成，场面十分壮观。

“降狮会”是群众自发组织的表演降狮舞的演出团体。杨乃让的祖父和父亲均为降狮会的主要成员。杨乃让受祖父和父亲影响，自幼喜爱柳林降狮舞。柳林降狮舞表演独特，伴奏恢宏，给杨乃让留下了深刻的童年记忆，一直伴随着他的成长。

杨乃让为柳林降狮舞的传承与发展做出了重要贡献。在降狮舞停演多年之后，杨乃让求教本村多位降狮舞老艺人，系统整理出“狮舞”的全套故事情节、文字资料、戏中道白，并基本熟悉了整套鼓点，在原来的基础上修改了部分戏文、道白。杨乃让还偕同兄弟杨乃富、杨乃毅自费修复降狮舞的传世服装道具，购置装备、乐器等，使降狮舞得以恢复，重新在民间艺术的舞台上展现魅力。

功夫不负有心人，经过努力，越来越多的人认识了冠县柳林降狮舞这一传统舞蹈。杨乃让在传承的道路上不断前进，多次在市、县民间艺术会演中获奖，聊城电视台也曾以此传统舞蹈为题材进行专题报道，提高了冠县柳林降狮舞的知名度，促进了其传承与传播。

Yang Nairang—
Inheritor of Liulin Lion Taming Dance

Yang Nairang, male, was born in 1963 in Guan County, Liaocheng City, Shandong Province. Mr. Yang is the ninth-generation inheritor of Liulin lion taming dance.

Liulin lion taming dance is a folk dance in Liulin Town (right on the border between Hebei, Shandong and Henan Provinces), Guan County, Liaocheng City, Shandong Province. The dance comes from Tangyi County (now the Tangyi Town in Dongchangfu District in Liaocheng City) in the early stages of the Qing Dynasty, boasting a history of more than 300 years. The dance depicts a lion trainer tracking, locating, fighting and finally taming two lions with Ganoderma lucidum, a hook and a flag of yin and yang. There are various types of dance movements, including "Stepping on the Drum" "Tracking the Lions' Footprints" "Fighting the Lion" "Casting the Flag" and "Stepping on the Four Doors", which are accompanied by drums and gongs.

The original organization of the Liulin lion taming dance was named "Liulin Lion Taming Association", which was founded by the lovers of the dance. Yang Nairang's grandfather and father are key members of the assosiation. Influenced by his grandfather and father, Mr. Yang was deeply attracted by Liulin lion taming dance when he was a little boy. The spectacular performance and wonderful music left a deep and far-reaching impression on the little boy.

Yang Nairang made important contributions to the development and promotion of Liulin lion taming dance. The dance had been extinct for years. Mr. Yang later consulted the elder dancers in the village about the monologue, storyline and written records of the dance. He also learnt how to beat the drum during the performance and revised some monologues and lines. Mr. Yang, and his two brothers, Yang Naifu and Yang Naiyi, repaired the props and costumes handed down from ancient times, purchased equipment and musical instruments at their own expense, and finally brought Liulin lion taming dance back up to the stage.

Liulin lion taming dance has gained popularity. Yang Nairang has devoted his life to the development and promotion of the dance. He has won many awards on folk arts shows at the municipal and county level. Liulin lion taming dance was once covered by the TV Station of Liaocheng City, which helped to inherit and popularize the dance.

傳承人

传统戏剧

Traditional Drama

柳子戏（宋家班）传承人——刘进武

刘进武，男，1929 年出生，山东菏泽定陶人。

宋家班柳子戏的演出剧目内容丰富，既有三国戏，又有水浒戏。武戏吸收了民间的真刀真枪，赤膊“彩戏”，很受欢迎，因此民间传有：“不看花衣裳，也要看柳子戏的光脊梁。”其伴奏“三大件”为笛、笙、三弦，人称“笛似骨，笙似肉，弦似筋”，伴奏时音域广阔，音色亮丽，节奏明快，转换自如流畅，个性明显华丽，韵味醇厚，优美动听。每个剧目唱腔各异，许多剧目每出戏从头至尾只用一种声腔。由于植根于民间，宋家班的柳子戏既有民间俗曲小令的基础，又有经历代文人加工修饰的过程，因此呈现出雅俗共赏且与民俗文化相融合的特征。

宋家班以“冬”字辈起头排序，传承谱系明确。1933 年，宋楼村创建了第一个柳子戏科班，凭着对戏剧的热爱，刘进武于 1946 年开始学戏，成为宋家班“金”字辈学员，是宋家班第二代旦角传承人。1953 年，宋家班落户郓城并成立了“工农剧团”，参加华东会演，获得极大反响；1956 年刘进武率团参加了曲阜孔庙会演，荣获一等奖。

刘进武登台演出后经常参演《白兔记》《金锁记》《孙安动本》《玩会跳船》《抱妆盒》《燕青打擂》《三盗芭蕉扇》《春草闯堂》《打登州》《御碑亭》《红罗记》《恩仇记》等几十个剧目，所塑造的角色深受观众的喜爱。

1960 年，刘进武开始担任定陶柳子戏宋家班剧团团长，与团内其他人员在家乡演出并授徒，培养了一批知名的柳子戏演员，为柳子戏的传承做出了突出贡献。

Liu Jinwu—
Inheritor of the Song's Liuzi Opera

Liu Jinwu, male, was born in 1929 in Dingtao District, Heze City, Shandong Province.

The Song's Liuzi opera has many plays, including the plays about "Romance of the Three Kingdoms" and "Water Margin". The barebacked martial arts performers use real swords and spears, so the fighting is exciting and attracts many people. The locals comment that the fight in Liuzi opera performance is worth watching. Liuzi opera is usually accompanied by a sanxian (a three stringed instrument), a flute and a sheng (a woodwind instrument). The music features bright timbre and fast rhythm. Different plays have different tunes, and many plays have only one tune throughout the whole play. Liuzi opera has song lyrics written by both less and highly educated people, thus making it catering to the tastes of all social classes.

The Song's Liuzi Opera Troupe has numbered different groups of members using different Chinese characters. The earliest members were "Dong" members. In 1933, the first Liuzi opera troupe was founded in Songlou Village. In 1946, Liu Jinwu started to learn the opera with great enthusiasm and became a "Jin" member. He is the second-generation female role in the Song's Liuzi Opera Troupe. In 1953, the Song's Liuzi Opera Troupe moved to Yucheng and set up the Workers and Peasants Troupe. The troupe later participated in the Eastern China Arts and Culture Joint Show and the performance was a great success. In 1956, Mr. Liu led other dancers to participate in the Confucius Temple Arts and Culture Joint Show in Qufu, Shandong Province, and won the first prize.

Liu Jinwu has played many roles in plays such as "A Story of a White Rabbit" "A story of Golden Lock" "Sun An's Accusation" "Meeting on the Boat" "Carrying the Box" "Yan Qing Fighting on a Platform" "Stealing Palm-Leaf Fan" "Chuncao Disturbing the Court" "An Attack On Dengzhou" "Yubei Pavilion" "A Story of Red Cloth" and "A Story of Revenge", which are liked by the audience.

In 1960, Liu Jinwu started to serve as the head of the Song's Liuzi Opera Troupe in Dingtao District. He performed and taught the opera with other actors of the troupe in his hometown, trained a group of well-known Liuzi opera actors, and made significant contributions to the development and promotion of Liuzi opera.

柳子戏（宋家班）传承人——赵新文

赵新文，男，1947 年出生，山东菏泽定陶人。

柳子戏，又名“弦子戏”，亦称“北调子”，是山东主要地方戏之一。柳子戏有近 500 年的历史，传统剧目有 200 余出，音乐唱腔曲牌 600 余支，调式分为越调、平调下调、二八调、反工四调和转调，一般以前四调为主。主要伴奏乐器为曲笛、笙、小三弦，俗称“三大件”。唱词是以长短句为主，主要通过挂“序”（齐言体）的手法，两者交错演唱，变化无穷，多姿多彩。由于宫调繁多，音乐优美，唱腔典雅古朴、清新绵邈，柳子戏素有“九腔十八调，七十二哎咳”和“百调子”之称。

赵新文师从苗月芹、李广连（济宁嘉祥柳子班负责人）、郑兰亭以及李永秀（定陶宋楼柳子班主要演员，曾任菏泽地区柳子剧团文武小生演员、山东省柳子剧团演员）。他主攻文武小生，表演基本功扎实，身段规范，在继承传统唱腔的基础上，采用科学的发声方法，吸收其他的声腔精华，融会贯通，其声音清脆圆润，具有穿透力；同时可根据角色需要，行腔收放自如，咬字吐字极为讲究，以情带声，以字带声。

赵新文从艺以来，曾主演《白兔记》中的刘承佑、《抱妆盒》中的陈琳、《婚书》中的辛文秀、《包公错断》中的颜查散、《火焰山》中的孙悟空《对松关》中的罗章及现代戏《奇袭白虎团》中的严伟才、《南海长城》中的区英才、《红嫂》中的彭排长、《白毛女》中的大春等，塑造了许多个性鲜明的角色。

多年来，赵新文一直致力于柳子戏的传承工作。1999 年为培养柳子戏接班人，赵新文创办了柳子班，身为主要负责人和唱腔教师，带领全体人员，克服困难，全身心投入教学和管理工作中，其辅导的学生多人获奖。2004 年，赵新文获中国戏剧家协会颁发的“培育新人奖”。

Zhao Xinwen—
Inheritor of the Song's Liuzi Opera

Zhao Xinwen, male, was born in 1947 in Dingtao District, Heze City, Shandong Province.

Liuzi opera (also known as Xianzi opera, or Beidiaozi) is a major local opera in Shandong Province, boasting a history of nearly 500 years. There are more than 200 traditional plays, and more than 600 tunes, which can be divided into five diao (keys) named yuediao, pingdiaoxiadiao, erbadiao, fangongsidiao and zhuandiao separately (the former four are most commonly used tunes). Liuzi opera is usually accompanied by a sanxian (a three stringed instrument), a flute and a sheng (a woodwind instrument). The song lyrics have lines of different characters, which brings more changes. Liuzi opera features various gongdiao (keys) and traditional tunes, and is regarded as a vast pool of keys and tunes.

Zhao Xinwen has learn Liuzi opera under the guidance of Miao Yueqin, Li Guanglian (the head of Liuzi Opera Troupe in Jiaxiang County), Zheng Lanting and Li Yongxiu. Li Yongxiu was a leading actor of the Liuzi Opera Troup in Songlou Village, Dingtao District, and once both a Wen Sheng (male actor specializing in singing and reciting) and a Wu Sheng (male actor skilled in stage-fighting) of Liuzi Opera Troup in Heze and an actor of the Liuzi Troupe of Shandong Province. Mr. Zhao is a wusheng with a fine figure and good technique. Not only has he mastered the traditional tunes of Liuzi opera, but he has also adopted scientific singing methods, and absorbed the tunes of other folk operas in his performance. Mr. Zhao has a beautiful, clear and penetrating singing voice. He can change his voice when playing different roles and sing the lyrics clearly and with emotions.

Zhao Xinwen has played the characters like Liu Chengyou in “A Story of a White Rabbit”, Chen Lin in “Carrying the Box”, Xin Wenxiu in “Marriage Certificate”, Yan Chasan in “Bao Zheng's Wrongful Conviction”, the Monkey King in “Flaming Mountains”, Luo Zhang in “Xi Qin Conquering the West”, Yan Weicai in “A Surprise Attack on White Tiger Troop”, Qu Yingcai in “The Border Fence on the South China Sea”, Peng Lin in “Yimeng Sister-in-Law”, and Dachun in “The White-Haired Girl”. Mr. Zhao has brought real life into his characters.

Over the years, Zhao Xinwen has been working to promote Liuzi opera. In 1999, Mr. Zhao founded a Liuzi opera troupe to teach and promote the opera. He devoted himself into the teaching and management of the troupe and had overcome many difficulties with the troupe members. Many of his students won many awards. In 2004, the China Theatre Association presented Mr. Zhao with an award for his work in teaching Liuzi opera.

吕剧传承人——王永昌

王永昌，男，1936年出生，滨州人，山东省著名吕剧作曲家。

吕剧起源于鲁东北一带，是山东地区最具代表性的剧种之一，至今已有100多年的历史。纵观吕剧艺术的演变发展过程，大体经过了山东琴书—化装扬琴—定名吕剧三个阶段。作为山东吕剧领军人物之一的王永昌，参与了吕剧的建设和传承工作。

1956年，王永昌进入广饶县吕剧团任音乐教师，期间向东路琴书老艺人商业兴拜师学艺，亲口学唱并记录了《小姑贤》《王婆骂鸡》和《坐楼》等全剧的唱谱。1969年，他被调到惠民地区（现在的滨州市）吕剧团。在长期坚持自修音乐基本理论的基础上，王永昌又于1991~1994四年中完成了由中国音协主办的“中国函授音乐学院”的专业化学习。多年的工作经验为王永昌创造吕剧抒情体奠定了坚实的基础。

王永昌新创吕剧【四平慢板】，不仅弥补了戏剧内容在广度和深度上的不足，同时也满足了观众对更为抒情、柔美的板腔的需要。在从事吕剧创作50多年中，王永昌坚持走访民间艺人，取材于民，亲口学唱当面记谱，先后为吕剧演出剧目作曲150余出。在长期的实践、演出、交流与考评中，他逐渐总结出吕剧声腔音乐的基本特征及其“快简慢繁，微变渐进，一曲多用，变不离宗”的发展规律。

王永昌更新了吕剧音乐的基调，拓宽了吕剧板腔的功能，还口传心授培育了优秀演员史萍和作曲家王铁。其作品多次在省内外获高奖并在国家级音乐论坛发表文章，如《谈吕剧创腔中的调性转换手法》《吕剧传统音乐简说》和《寻求戏曲传统音乐与现代剧人物性格的凝聚点》等共7篇。这不仅为吕剧研究者提供了宝贵的资料，也让更多人有机会了解吕剧，大大推动了吕剧的传播。

Wang Yongchang—Inheritor of Lü Opera

Wang Yongchang, male, was born in 1936 in Binzhou City, Shandong Province. He is a well-known Lü opera composer.

As Shandong's most representative local opera, Lü opera was originated in the northeast Shandong with a history of over 100 years. It went through three stages, namely Shandong qinshu, make-up yangqin (Chinese hammered dulcimer), and the current Lü opera. Mr. Wang has been involved in its development and become an inheritor.

In 1956, Wang Yongchang began to teach music in the Guangrao Lü opera Troupe during which time he learned from Shang Yexing, a master at East Shandong Qinshu, singing and recording the complete lyrics of "Sister-in-Law" "Old Lady Wang Curses the Chickens" "A Story of Song Jiang and His Wife", etc. Starting from 1969, Mr. Wang worked for Binzhou (then Huimin Area) Lü opera Troupe. While constantly learning basic theories of music by self-study, he finished professional learning through the correspondence course of Chinese Music Academy sponsored by Chinese Music Association from 1991 to 1994. Years of working and studying experience has laid the foundation for creating the lyrical singing style of Lü opera.

Wang Yongchang created the tone of siping manban (largo) that enriched the Lü opera and met the need of the audience for a more lyrical and graceful banqiang style (literally "beat and tune style"). More than 50 years has witnessed Mr. Wang's efforts to develop Lü opera—he composed over 150 pieces of music for the performance of Lü opera based on what he learned and recorded from folk artists he had visited. Through years of practice, performance, communication and evaluation, Mr. Wang gradually concluded the following basic characteristics of the tunes in Lü opera and its law of development: easy notes in a quick tune and difficult notes in a slow one, progressive change in tunes, one tune with serval variations while remaining its original style.

Except developing both the tones and the banqiang style of Lü opera, Wang Yongchang also trained Shi Ping, a good performer now, and Wang Tie, a good composer now. Mr. Wang's works have won prizes at provincial level for many times and his seven papers were published in music forums at national level, such as "A Study on Modulation Techniques in Creation of a Key in Lü Opera" "A Brief Study on Traditional Tones of Lü Opera" and "Common Features between Traditional and Modern Characters in Lü Opera". These works are valuable for studying Lü opera and beneficial for its spread to a large extent with more opportunities for people to know it.

吕剧传承人——胡静华

胡静华，女，1964年出生，山东济宁人，国家一级演员，中国戏剧家协会会员、省戏剧家协会会员。

吕剧是山东最具代表性的地方剧种之一，曾名“化装扬琴”“琴戏”，是在民间说唱艺术山东琴书(坐腔扬琴)的基础上吸收民间艺术花鼓、小曲、扽腔等发展演变而来的，迄今已有100多年的历史。吕剧的剧目大体可分两种：一种是小戏和单出戏如《小姑贤》《借年》《王定保借当》等；一种是连台本戏，多根据鼓词改编而来，如《金鞭记》《金镯玉环记》《五女兴唐》等。

1997年，胡静华入山东省吕剧院工作。2001年，拜著名吕剧表演艺术家郎咸芬为师，系统地学习吕剧表演艺术。在老师的辛勤培育下，胡静华刻苦努力，积极参加舞台演出实践，深得吕剧表演艺术的精髓。

在向老一辈艺术家学习的同时，胡静华继承和发扬了吕剧表演艺术，逐步形成了自己独特的吕剧表演艺术风格。她的表演朴实大方，情景交融，人物特色鲜明；唱腔高亢洪亮，声情并茂，刚柔兼备；吐字清晰，韵味醇厚，娓娓动听，深受同行的好评和广大观众的喜爱。

胡静华在吕剧《李二嫂改嫁》《苦菜花》《红嫂》《师魂》《小姑贤》《柳叶青》《补天》《大唐黜官记》等众多剧目中担任主要角色。胡静华在吕剧《苦菜花》中成功塑造了母亲的形象，并受到专家和全国广大观众的认可，参演的大型吕剧《补天》获国家“十大精品剧目”奖。胡静华曾荣获中国戏剧节“表演奖”，多次获得山东省艺术节“表演一等奖”“表演二等奖”，2007年获得“十大吕剧名家”称号。

Hu Jinghua—Inheritor of Lü Opera

Hu Jinghua, female, was born in 1964 in Jining City, Shandong Province. She is a national first-class actress and a member of the China Theatre Association and Shandong Theatre Association.

Lü opera, Shandong's most representative local opera with over 100 years of history, was previously known as make-up yangqin or qinxi. It was developed from Shangdong Qinshu (zuoqiang Yangqin, a folk art combines singing and narrating), and borrowed the features of some folk arts like flower drama, ballads, and denqiang. Lü opera has two types of performance. The first type is short plays and non-serial plays such as "Sister-in-Law" "To Borrow for the Spring Festival" and "Wang Dingbao Pawning the Dowry of His Fiancée". The other type is serial plays, adapted from Guci (a folk art a ccompanied by drum), such as "The Romance of Hu Yanqing" "The Love Story of Baotong" and "Five Heroines of the Tang Dynasty".

Starting from 1997, Hu Jinghua worked for Shandong Lü Opera Troupe, and since 2001, she systematically learned how to perform under the guidance of Lang Xianfen, a renowned Lü opera performer. Through years of hard work and active participation in live performances, she has comprehended the essence of Lü opera.

Based on what she had learned from the senior artists, Hu Jinghua inherited the performing arts of Lü opera and developed her own style. She sings naturally and attractively in a high, clear, mellow but flexible voice. She precisely conveys the distinctive characteristics of the figures and gains the praise and love from her peers and audience.

Hu Jinghua played main roles in many Lü operas such as "The Remarriage of Mrs. Li" "Bitter Cauliflower" "Sister Hong" "The Soul of a Teacher" "Sister-in-Law" "Green Willow Leaves" "Patching up the Sky" and "Dismissing Officials by Emperor Taizong of Tang Dynasty". The mother she played in "Bitter Cauliflower" was highly recognized by both experts and a wide audience, and the opera "Patching up the Sky" she participated in won the national Top Ten Selected Plays Award. Honored as the "Top Ten Lü Opera Performers" in 2007, Ms. Hu also received the Performance Award in Chinese Theatre Festival and for many times won the first prize and the second prize on art performance at the Shandong Cultural and Art Festival.

吕剧传承人——马常委

马常委，男，1959年出生，山东临朐人，国家一级演奏员。

吕剧是山东最具代表性的地方剧种，曾名“化装扬琴”“琴戏”，是在民间说唱艺术山东琴书(坐腔扬琴)的基础上吸收民间艺术花鼓、小曲、扽腔等发展演变而来的，迄今已有100多年的历史。吕剧的唱腔以板腔体为主，兼唱曲牌。曲调简单朴实，优美动听，灵活顺口，易学易唱。吕剧的伴奏乐器分为文场和武场。文场主要乐器是坠琴、扬琴，其次为二胡、三弦、琵琶、笛子、唢呐等，乐器可视剧情酌情增减。武场伴奏乐器主要有皮鼓、板、大锣、小锣、大铙钹、堂鼓等。

1980年，马常委拜著名吕剧音乐专家、坠琴演奏大师李渔为师，攻吕剧坠琴演奏和吕剧作曲，在几十年的艺术生涯中，广撷博采，刻苦学习，深得老师的真传，为吕剧坠琴演奏的传承与发展做出了突出贡献。

马常委长期为郎咸芬、林建华、李岱江等吕剧名家伴奏，主要伴奏剧目有《李二嫂改嫁》《姊妹易嫁》《借年》等。在传承老一辈坠琴演奏技艺的基础上，马常委集众家之长，潜心研究，从而总结出坠琴不仅是伴奏乐器，而且作为主奏乐器，坠琴可以描绘人物心态情貌、勾勒广阔的生活画面，从而达到“器写人声”的艺术境界。他的演奏刚柔相济，舒展流畅，琴声似语，韵味隽永，楚楚动人，换弓无迹，换指无痕。马常委在多年的艺术实践中形成了独特的演奏风格，被称为“中国吕剧第一琴”，享有很高的赞誉。

马常委曾多次获得国家级、省级优秀伴奏奖。1986年7月在全国首次戏曲现代戏优秀唱段评奖活动中，他伴奏的《豆腐西施》《香蒲》获得演奏艺术奖。2012年吕剧《砖头记》获“山东省小戏展演最佳音乐奖”；2013年吕剧《百姓书记》获“第十届中国艺术节文华音乐(作曲奖)”。他还曾出访过许多海外国家和地区，努力将吕剧艺术传播发扬。

Ma Changwei—Inheritor of Lü Opera

Ma Changwei, male, was born in 1959 in Linqu City, Shandong Province. He is a national first-class actor.

Lü opera, Shandong's most representative local opera with over 100 years of history, was previously known as make-up yangqin or qinxi. It was developed from Shangdong Qinshu (zuoqiang Yangqin, a folk art combines singing and narrating), and borrowed the features of some folk arts like flower drama, ballads, and denqiang. The Lü opera takes banqiang and qupai as major tunes. With its simple and vivid lyrics, beautiful melodies, and rich and colorful lines, Lü opera is easy to learn. Its instruments are classified into two parts: Wenchang (instruments of the orchestra) and Wuchang (percussion instruments). The former includes zhuiqin and yangqin particularly as well as erhu, sanxian, pipa, Chinese bamboo flute, suona and so on, while how to use these instruments depends on the specific opera. The latter includes leather drum, hardwood clappers, large gong, small gong, Chinese crotales, tanggu and so on.

Since 1980, Ma Changwei formally acknowledged Li Yu, an expert in Lü opera music and zhuiqin as his teacher to further his study on composing the opera and playing zhuiqin. With decades of performing experience, he has worked on the Lü opera and fully understood the essence of the art from his teacher, and made great contribution to the inheritance and spreading of Lü opera.

Ma Changwei has played for many distinguished performers like Lang Xianfen, Lin Jianhua, Li Daijiang. The main operas he accompanied were "The Remarriage of Mrs. Li" "Marrying Sister's Fiancé" and "To Borrow for the Spring Festival". Learning from senior performers, Mr. Ma takes zhuiqin as not only an instrument but also an indicator of a character's inner world and a picture of life in many aspects. In other words, zhuiqin interprets life in a musical way. His music, a perfect mixture of vigor and softness, sounds like someone telling a story gently. His music goes smoothly and flexibly, and attracts the audience deeply. Through years of practice, he has formed his own performing style, is recognized as China's best zhuiqin player.

Ma Changwei has won many accompaniment prizes at the national and provincial levels for his excellent performance. In July 1986, at the first national selection of excellent modern operas, the works he accompanied, "Tofu Beauty" and "The Pu Family", were awarded for his excellent playing. Mr. Ma also visited some countries overseas to promote the spread of Lü opera.

茂腔传承人——张梅香

张梅香，女，1950 年出生，山东胶州人，国家一级演员。

茂腔源于明代中叶的肘鼓子，民间艺人吸取各地肘鼓子之长，糅进本地民间小调“老拐调”，结合苏北“海冒调”，形成了新唱法，称之为“茂肘鼓”。中华人民共和国成立后，正式定名为“茂腔”。茂腔曲调质朴自然，唱腔通俗易懂，地方特色浓郁，深受群众喜爱。

1970 年，张梅香进入青岛市茂腔剧团，师承曾金凤老师，工青衣、花旦。1976 年，张梅香在《朝阳沟》一戏中担任主角银环后走红，成名后的张梅香不断探索，逐渐形成了自己的艺术风格。她以茂腔音乐的基本曲调为基调，以当地方言特征为基本出发点，使得音乐语言化，亲切又新颖。张梅香广泛学习民间小调、西洋美声及民族戏曲等的演唱技巧，结合自身嗓音甜润、音域宽的特点，形成了以气驭声、以声托情、声情并茂的演唱方法。张梅香也善于把握人物的情感线和行动依据，以恰当的唱腔和动作细节展示人物复杂的内心世界，塑造了众多个性鲜明的舞台形象。

从艺以来，张梅香在 60 余出大型剧目中担任主要角色，其中 10 余出为新创作剧目。她还被山东省文化厅授予“尖子演员”“送文化下乡先进个人”称号。2002 年，在全国老年文艺会演中获金奖；2003 年，在全国“国花杯”戏曲演员大赛中获“十佳花旦金奖”；2004 年，在山东省老年大学文艺会演中获一等奖；2005~2007 年，先后录制 8 出茂腔传统戏 VCD 光盘出版发行。

张梅香退休之后在多所老年大学创办茂腔班，先后培训学员数百名；深入学校教习传统茂腔唱段，培养少年儿童对茂腔艺术的兴趣；在 2006 年茂腔被列入“国家级非物质文化遗产”之后，积极参加相关的纪念、庆祝等演出活动，至今仍为茂腔的传承发展贡献力量。

Zhang Meixiang—Inheritor of Maoqiang Opera

Zhang Meixiang, female, was born in 1950 in Jiaozhou City, Shandong Province. She is a national first-class actress.

Maoqiang opera is formed on the basis of the folk music Zhouguzi in the Mid-Ming Dynasty. The folk artists then incorporated into Zhouguzi their local ditty named "Laoguai" and a ditty called "Haimao" northern Jiangsu, so a new singing method named Mao came into existence. It was officially named Maoqiang opera after the founding of the People's Republic of China in 1949. It is well loved by people for its simple and natural tunes and rhythm, easy-to-understand vocal performance, and brimming with local history and culture.

Zhang Meixiang joined in Qingdao Maoqiang Opera Troupe in 1970, where she was trained by Zeng Jinfeng, who played Qing Yi and Hua Dan, respectively representing young or middle-aged women with gentle and refined dispositions and young women with frank and open personalities. In 1976, her career took off after she played the leading role Yinhuan in the drama "Chaoyang Village" and gradually found her own performing style after years of learning and improving. She sings in a novel yet genial way that is close to people's everyday life, employing the basic tunes of Maoqiang opera and local dialects. Ms. Zhang has also developed a singing method that utilizes breath, voice and emotion at the same time to the largest extent, upgraded by her sweet voice, wide vocal range, and extensive learning of the singing skills of folk ditties, Western vocal music and national operas. She is also a master at portraying graceful images with distinctive characteristics, through capturing the emotions and complex inner world of the characters and acting them out via accurate vocals and detailed body performance.

Since she started the career as an actress, Zhang Meixiang has played the main characters in some 60 large-scale traditional Chinese operas, more than 10 of which are created lately. She was given the title of "Top Actor and Advanced Individual for Bringing Culture to the Countryside" by Shandong Provincial Department of Culture. In 2002, she won the gold medal in the National Senior Citizens Art and Cultural Performance; in 2003, she brought home the Top Ten Hua Dan Gold Award in the National Flower Cup, a Chinese opera competition; In 2004, she won the first prize in the Art and Cultural Performance of Shandong University for the Elderly; VCD disks of eight Maoqiang opera plays she starred in from 2005 to 2007 were published.

After her retirement, Zhang started to offer Maoqiang opera classes in several universities for the elderly and taught hurdreds of students. She chose primary schools as the starting point to cultivate children's interest in traditional Maoqiang opera. After it was listed as the first batch of National Intangible Cultural Heritage in 2006, She took an even more active part in activities commemorating or celebrating such a feat. She is always dedicated to the inheritance and promotion of the traditional art.

山亭皮影戏传承人——陈守科

陈守科，男，1960年出生，枣庄山亭人。山亭皮影戏第四代传承人。

山亭皮影戏作为独具特色的皮影戏，其舞台设施简单，真人演员少，道具多，一人负责锣鼓钗梆，一人演唱打斗，可包二三十人的大本戏。其中民间气息较浓厚，故事短小精悍；大本戏像连续剧一样节节相连、引人入胜；传统剧目丰富，唱词生动，唱腔独特。山亭皮影戏在唱、挑、刻画等方面呈现出不同的特色，如唱腔一律为唱经调，念佛韵一手操作8个人物完成不同动作（骑马转身、云端上翻滚等）。其门派特点鲜明，唱腔、雕刻、绘画、上色、鼓点和任何地方的皮影戏都有较大不同。

陈守科出身皮影世家，7岁随父陈德义学艺，因为皮影戏必须具备童子功夫才能手法灵活、唱腔优美一致，所以父亲对他的要求极为严格。严师出高徒，陈守科12岁时就能登台演出，16岁替父带徒，现已从事皮影事业40余年。通过大量的实践，陈守科意识到只有在保持老剧目的基础上，大力创作新剧目，与时俱进，才能使这门艺术不衰。为此在保留了《杨家将》《水浒传》《东游记》《西游记》等传统剧目之外，陈守科不断创作新剧目，如《张普善永远活在我们心中》《景区来了孙大圣》《五福娃贺奥运》等。此外，陈守科还保留了前辈留下的皮影人物880余件，皮影配件160余套，具备绘画、雕刻、挑、唱、演奏全面技法，为山亭皮影戏的保护和传承做出了重要贡献。

多年来，陈守科一直致力于山亭皮影戏的传承。2007年，陈守科成立皮影研究所，自办学校，免费招收学员。2008年，台湾记者团对山亭皮影戏进行专访。山亭皮影戏的演出经常受到各级领导和广大人民群众的好评。

Chen Shouke—Inheritor of Shanting Shadow Puppetry

Chen Shouke, male, was born in 1960 in the Shanting District, Zaozhuang City, Shandong Province. He is the fourth-generation inheritor of Shanting shadow puppetry.

Shanting shadow puppetry, unlike other shadow plays, involves simple facilities, a few performers and numerous props. One performer plays gongs, drums and cymbals, and the other sings and manipulates puppets. They can do the job of a big play that would have needed 20 to 30 performers. The play is a vivid demonstration of folk life through concise yet intriguing stories. A big play is as absorbing and fascinating as serial shows. Traditional plays of all sorts are told through catchy lyrics and unique vocals. Shanting shadow play exhibits distinctive features with regard to drawing, craving, coloring, manipulating, singing and drumming. For instance, only Jing tune is allowed. Some masters can even skillfully manipulate eight figures at the same time for them to appear to ride a horse and roll in the clouds.

Chen Shouke, born in a shadow puppetry playing family, began to study it at the age of seven under the guidance of his father Chen Deyi. To skillfully manipulate the puppets and narrate a story in a pretty tune, the performers require tons of training and practice ever since a very young age. Having gone through the rigorous training of his father's, Chen was able to perform on stage at the age of 12 and train pupils at age 16. Now he is a master of the play after having been in the industry for more than 40 years. After performing for all these years, Mr. Chen is clear that, to keep this traditional folk art alive and abreast of the times, the artists must push the play across new frontiers while preserving its original charm. To meet this end, aside from traditional plays such as "The Generals of the Yang Family" "Water Margin" "Journey to the East" and "Journey to the West", Mr. Chen keeps enlarging his repertory by writing new ones including "Forever in Our Heart" "Zhang Pushan" "Monkey King Coming to Scenic Spots" and "Five Fuwa of Beijing Celebrating the Olympics" . In addition, Mr. Chen saves more than 880 shadow puppets left by his predecessors along with more than 160 sets of accessories, and is skilled in techniques concerning, drawing, craving, manipulating singing and drumming. He has always been a crucial figure in protecting and promoting Shanting shadow puppetry.

Chen Shouke has been committed to inheriting and promoting Shanting shadow play for years. He established a research institute and a school for shadow puppetry offering free training for students in 2007. In 2008, a team of Taiwan journalists conducted an exclusive interview with performers of Shanting shadow puppetry. The play is favored and applauded by audience from all walks of life.

京剧传承人——白云明

白云明，男，1945年出生，山东济南人，全国文化系统先进工作者。

京剧在山东具有较为悠久的历史。据不完全统计，清中后期至民国初年，山东各地出现过100多个京剧科班，京剧史上绝大多数著名演员均曾多次来山东演出，如梅兰芳、尚小云、程砚秋、荀慧生、马连良、袁世海、裘盛戎、叶盛兰等名家。中华人民共和国成立后，山东各地市大多成立了京剧团。京剧各大流派在山东均有知名演员。

白云明的父亲是著名京剧武生白玉昆先生。白玉昆先生嗓音宽亮、道白清楚、戏路宽广，他在20世纪50年代来到山东工作，晚年主要从事戏曲教育事业，为山东戏曲人才的培养做出了重要贡献。他创作的众多武生剧目，如《精忠传》《天雨花》《疯僧扫秦》等，受到了社会各界的高度赞扬和热烈欢迎。白玉昆先生勇于创新，尊重传统而又不墨守陈规。他集众家所长，在京剧界的历史上产生过重要影响，尤其是他的“出手”更堪称一绝。

白云明自幼随父学艺，5岁登台演出，继承了其父亲的艺术风格，并结合自身特点，创作、演出了新的剧目，如《八仙斗白猿》《孙悟空大闹乾坤》等。

白云明培养了众多学生，他们目前大多已成为京剧舞台上的顶梁人物。白云明虽年事已高，但仍兼任导演工作，排演了众多的传统剧目和新编剧目，如《奇袭白虎团》《春秋霸主》《铁道游击队》《郑和下西洋》等，曾获“文华导演奖”和中国京剧节金奖等。1995年，获“全国文化系统先进工作者”称号，为京剧的传承和发展做出了重要贡献。

Bai Yunming—Inheritor of Peking Opera

Bai Yunming, male, was born in 1945 in Jinan City, Shandong Province. He is a national advanced worker in cultural system.

Peking opera has enjoyed a steady development in Shandong for a long time. According to incomplete statistics, over 100 opera schools existed in different parts of Shandong from the middle and late Qing Dynasty to the early years of the Republic of China. Most famous Peking opera actors in history have performed in Shandong for a long time, including Peking opera masters such as Mei Lanfang, Shang Xiaoyun, Cheng Yanqiu, Xun Huisheng, Ma Lianliang, Yuan Shihai, Qiu Shengrong, and Ye Shenglan. After the establishment of People's Republic of China, prefectural and municipal Peking opera troupes have been established. Shandong has fostered famous actors for major schools of Peking opera.

Bai Yunming's father is Bai Yukun, a famous Lao Sheng (senior male role) actor, who sings in a high, shrill voice, articulates his lines, and is able to act various roles. Mr. Bai came to Shandong in 1950s and was engaged in opera education in his later years, making great contribution to the cultivation of opera talents in Shandong. Many Peking operas he created with Wu Sheng as the main character, such as "The Life of Yue Fei" "Rain Flowers" and "The Crazy Monk Sweeps Out the Tyrant", have been highly appreciated and warmly welcomed by people of all walks of life. Mr. Bai has innovative spirits and values tradition, but never falls into stereotypes, all of which allow him to learn from different schools of Peking opera. He is an important figure in the history of Peking opera and has impressed people with his Chu Shou, a kind of martial art in Peking opera.

Following his father, Bai Yunming started to learn Peking opera since he was a child and made his debut at the age of 5. He inherited his father's artistic style and created new plays based on his own characteristics, such as "Eight Immortals Fight the White Ape" and "The Havoc in Heaven".

Many of Mr. Bai's students have become top performers of Peking opera. Mr. Bai himself, despite advanced age, still holds concurrent post of director, directing numerous traditional and modern plays such as "Raid on the White Tiger Regiment" "Lords of the Spring and Autumn Period" "Railroad Guerrilla" and "Zheng He's Voyages". Mr. Bai has been honored the "Wen Hua Award for Director" and Gold Award of the China Peking Opera Festival. In 1995, Bai won the title of "National Advanced Worker in Cultural System" for his contribution to the inheritance and development of Peking opera.

京剧传承人——王玉瑾

王玉瑾，男，1937 年出生，山东济南人，国家一级演员。

京剧的行当全面，表演成熟，气势宏美。京剧分为生、旦、净、丑四大行当，京剧界中有句俗话叫“无丑不成戏”，足以看出“丑”这一行当对于一台剧目的重要性。虽然丑角在舞台艺术上是绿叶，但是红花也需绿叶配，众多优秀传统剧目都离不开丑行的陪衬，如在《玉堂春》《拾玉镯》《锁麟囊》《望江亭》《春草闯堂》等剧目中丑行都起到了衬托人物、烘托气氛的重要作用。

王玉瑾的启蒙老师是罗小奎、张文元先生。1960 年，他拜贾多才先生为师，随贾先生学习了众多文丑戏和彩旦戏。同时王玉瑾又向同行、前辈学习了四五十出戏中的大小角色，他既继承了前辈们的技艺和经验，又与时俱进，形成了有时代感的京剧丑角表演艺术。

王玉瑾博学众长，通过排练现代京剧，学到很多新的表演技巧，并与传统表演融会贯通，在不断地实践中，形成了鲜明的个人艺术风格。他所扮演的文丑、彩旦角色，做到了以情带念（念白），唱词和表演既规范又具有生活化，有激情而不低俗，既有戏又不夺戏。

王玉瑾在几十年的从艺生涯中塑造了众多的舞台形象，如《群英会》中的蒋干、《法门寺》中的贾桂、《铡美案》中的张三阳、《望江亭》中的杨衙内、《孔雀东南飞》中的焦母、《送亲演礼》中的陈氏、《拾玉镯》中的刘媒婆、《铁弓缘》中的陈母、现代京剧《红云岗》中的刁鬼等，他所塑造的人物形象性格突出、入木三分。1990 年，王玉瑾获山东省戏曲“八大名丑奖”。在收徒方面，他倾其所学，为京剧丑角演员业务水平的提高做出了重要贡献。

Wang Yujin—Inheritor of Peking Opera

Wang Yujin, male, was born in 1937 in Jinan City, Shandong Province. He is a national first-class actor.

Peking opera has a comprehensive classification of roles and a mature performing system with a magnificent acting style. Peking opera features four main role types, Sheng (gentlemen), Dan (women), Jing (rough men), and Chou (clowns). A saying in the Peking opera circle goes that "there is no play without Chou", showing the importance of Chou for Peking opera. Chou, though a secondary role on Peking opera's stage, serves as an important foil to main characters. Many excellent traditional plays will pale without Chou playing an important part in heightening the atmosphere and foiling roles in plays including "The Story of Sue San" "Pick Up the Jade Bracelet" "An Embroidered Treasure Pouch" "Wangjiang Pavilion" and "Chun Cao Makes Her Way into the Court".

Wang Yujing got into this career under the teaching of Luo Xiaokui and Zhang Wenyuan. In 1960, he formally acknowledged Jia Duocai as his teacher, learned to perform many Wen Chou (civilian roles such as merchants and jailers) and Cai Dan (clownish women) roles. Meanwhile, he took advice from fellow actors and predecessors on different roles in some 40 or 50 plays. With performing skills and experiences from predecessors, Mr. Wang has fostered his own acting style as Chou and kept pace with the times.

Wang Yujin learns new performing skills while playing modern Peking opera plays in rehearsals, and integrates them with the traditional ones, fostering a distinctive style in practices. While acting the Wen Chou and Cai Dan roles, he adds sentiments in the nianbai, a technique similar to the recitative, sings and performs in a normative but lively way. His acting style is passionate but never vulgar, adding color to the plays without overshadowing the leading role.

In decades of performing career, Wang Yujin has interpreted various roles: Jiang Gan in "A Gathering of Heroes", Jia Gui in "Famen Temple", Zhang Sanyang in "The Case of Chen Shimei", Yang Yanei in "Wangjiang Pavilion", Jiao Zhongqing's Mather in "The Peacock Flies Southeast", Matchmaker Liu in "Pick Up the Jade Bracelet", Chen's Mother in "The Story of Iron Bow", Diao Gui in "Hongyun Hills". The roles he interpreted are impressive with their distinctive characteristics. In 1990, Wang Yujing won the "Eight Top Clowns Award" of Shandong Province for his contribution to the inheritance and development of Peking opera.

京剧传承人——薛亚萍

薛亚萍，女，1946年出生，国家一级演员，享受国务院特殊津贴。

京剧旦角是京剧中扮演不同身份、不同年龄、不同性格的女性的一类角色的总称。旦行又分为青衣、花旦、刀马旦、武旦、老旦等，京剧历史上曾评选出“四大名旦”，即梅兰芳、尚小云、程砚秋、荀慧生，他们都曾为京剧的发展与传承做出了重大贡献。

薛亚萍出生于梨园世家，外祖父是京剧名净李春恒，母亲是京剧名旦李婉云。受家庭氛围的熏陶，薛亚萍自幼随母练功学戏，9岁登台演出；1962年，拜张君秋大师为师，刻苦钻研张派艺术；1969年，进入山东省京剧团工作；2010年，担任中国戏曲学院客座教授，为国家培养了许多优秀的京剧表演人才。

薛亚萍不但继承了张派艺术特殊的发声、演唱技巧，还根据个人所长，研究、发展了一套独特的表演方法。薛亚萍音域宽广，音色甜美，高低自如，穿透力强，极富艺术表现力。其高音区清脆明亮、中音区甜美柔和、低音区饱满厚重，演唱中新颖多变，有立体感。经过多年的艺术实践，薛亚萍的演唱不仅娇、媚、脆、水，而且嵌进了灵活圆润的喉音和清柔可人的鼻音。她的膛音酷似其师，演唱起来高而不尖，低而不沉，若断若续，收放粘连，寓华丽于端庄，在典雅中见深沉，极具大家风范。

薛亚萍曾在美国等国家和地区办班讲学，于海内外广泛传播京剧艺术。近年来，薛亚萍致力于打造优秀接班人、流派再传人，在坚持舞台演出的同时受聘于中国戏曲学院，担任研究生导师、流派班导师，悉心全方位授教，为京剧艺术的薪火相传做出了卓越贡献。1990年，薛亚萍荣获第八届中国戏剧梅花奖；1991年，获得全国中青年京剧演员电视大赛中年组最佳表演奖；1992年，获得“梅兰芳金奖大赛”的“梅兰芳金奖”，名列当代“中国八大名旦”之一；1994年，获得纽约文化局颁发的第二十二届“亚洲杰出艺人奖”；2002年，获得纽约美华艺术协会等机构主办的第十一届“终身艺术成就奖”。

Xue Yaping—Inheritor of Peking Opera

Xue Yaping, female, was born in 1946. She is a national first-class actress and an expert who enjoys the State Council Special Allowance.

In Peking opera, Dan is the general name for female roles of different ages and with various characteristics. The commonly seen ones are Zheng Dan (also known as Qingyi), Hua Dan, Daoma Dan, Wu Dan and Lao Dan. The four famous Dan actors of Peking opera, namely Mei Lanfang, Shang Xiaoyun, Cheng Yanqiu, and Xun Huisheng, have made great contribution to the inheritance and development of Peking opera.

Xue Yaping comes from a family of opera artists. Her grandfather is Li Chunheng, a well-known Jing actor of Peking opera, and her mother is Li Wanyun, also a famous Dan actress. Growing up in such a family, Xue Yaping started to learn Peking opera when she was a child and made her debut at 9 years old. In 1962, she formally acknowledged Zhang Qiujun, an opera master, as her teacher, delving into the Zhang's style. In 1969, she started to work in Peking opera Troupe of Shandong Province. In 2010, Xue Yaping was invited as the visiting professor of National Academy of Chinese Theatre Arts, and has cultivated many excellent opera performers.

Xue Yaping not only inherited the unique vocal and sing skills, but also developed a whole new performing method in her own style. She has a broad vocal range and sweet voice with perfect switching of soprano and contralto. Her singing style has penetrating power and great artistic appeal. Ms. Xue has a clear soprano, sweet and gentle mezzo-soprano, and deep contralto, which enables her to sing in a flexible and dramatic way. With years of performing experiences, Ms. Xue's performance has her own charm along with her firm guttural sound and soft nasal voice. Her sonorous voice is similar with that of her teacher.

Her perfect mixture of voice and the switching between the high and low notes enable her to perform in a wonderful way.

Xue Yaping has lectured in the United States, and other countries and regions, widely spreading Peking opera art at home and abroad. In recent years, Ms. Xue has been committed to fostering successors for her Zhang's style school of Peking opera. In spare time without performances, she serves as a tutor of postgraduates and the class of Peking opera schools, making great contribution to the inheritance of Peking opera with her devotion to teaching. In 1990, Ms. Xue was honored the 8th Plum Blossom Prize. In 1991, she won the Best Performance Award of the 2nd National TV Competition of Young and Middle-aged Performers. In 1992, she won the Mei Lanfang Gold Award, becoming one of the eight famous Dan artists in China. In 1994, she was honored the 22nd Asian Distinguished Artist Award by the New York City Department of Cultural Affairs. In 2002, she won the 11th Lifelong Achievement Award in an event organized by the New York Meihua Art Institute.

傳承人

曲艺
Folk Art Forms

东路大鼓传承人——丁淑红

丁淑红，女，1966 年出生，山东安丘人。

东路大鼓，又名“老东口”，是在山东东半部登州、莱州、青州三府农村土调大鼓基础上，吸收肘鼓子、莱阳弹词、茂腔等当地流行的曲艺音乐发展而成的一种民间鼓曲艺术形式。东路大鼓曲调较为婉转抒情，风格活泼清新，所以演唱书目多为民间传说、爱情故事。

丁淑红在中学时期就是学校里的文艺骨干。1986 年 1 月，以优异成绩考入闻名全国的庄户剧团——安丘市京剧团。在演唱京剧艺术的基础上学习吕剧、茂腔、黄梅戏等传统戏曲，后师从李及弟、王启宾、姜国治等曲艺名家，专攻东路大鼓的创作与表演。

经过多年的创作和说唱经验的积累，丁淑红逐渐形成了演唱细腻，声情并茂的东路大鼓演唱风格。她注重舞台形象美及“声”和“情”的有机结合，讲究唱曲兼唱情，从心灵深处打动观众。十多年来，每次演出时她总是着一身红色旗袍，左手轮月牙板，右手敲鼓板，板声清冽，鼓声骤起，手、眼、身、法、步皆有尺寸，煞是精神。

近五年来，她与妹妹丁丽华合作，深入基层演出了《林海雪原》《丁秀英盼夫》《战神》《俩老婆》《计划生育好》《科学发展观指航程》《咱百姓心中有颗星》等大鼓书和书帽 70 余种、670 多场次。在搞好日常工作的同时，丁淑红全身心投入到东路大鼓传习所的教学与实践中，坚持教学相长，培养了东路大鼓传人 74 名，为东路大鼓这一民间瑰宝的传承做出了重要贡献。

2008 年 10 月，丁淑红与妹妹创作演出的安丘大鼓《咱百姓心中有颗星》，被中共山东省纪委、山东省监察厅、山东文化厅授予全省基层廉政文艺创作展演三等奖。丁淑红与妹妹还连续 13 年参加了安丘市春节联欢晚会的东路大鼓表演，获得省、市、县级文艺演出奖项 16 次，演出曲目达 76 种。

Ding Shuhong—Inheritor of Donglu Drum

Ding Shuhong, female, was born in 1966, in Anqiu City, Shangdong.

Donglu drum, also known as "Laodongkou", is a folk drum music art form based on the rural local tunes of Dengzhou, Laizhou and Qinzhou, with influence from popular local folk art such as elbow drum, tanci of Laiyang, Maoqiang opera, etc. The melody of the Donglu drum tends to be implicit and lyric, and its style is dynamic and brisk. Folktales and love stories are the main themes of the drum performance.

Ding Shuhong has been a key member of the literature and art community since she attended high school. In January 1986, as one of the top candidates, she was admitted to Anqiu Peking Opera Troupe, which was a local farmers' troupe of national fame. She was taught to sing Peking opera, among other traditional dramas, such as the Lü opera, Maoqiang opera and Huangmei opera. Later on, she became a student of many drama masters, such as Li Jidi, Wang Qibin and Jiang Guozhi, and started to focus on the artistic creation performance of Donglu Drum.

After years of artistic creation and performance, she gradually developed her own style: exquisite performance with equal attention to voice and emotion. She focuses on the aesthetic image on the scene as well as an organic combination of voice and emotion. Singing the melody and conveying the emotion in an attempt to move her audience by heart is what she quests for. For more than ten years, she has shown up in every performance in a red cheongsam, with a crescent plate in the left hand and a clapper in the right. The clapper makes a crisp sound and the drum beats loudly. Every movement she makes represents the perfect harmony of her body and reveals her vigor.

In the past five years, Ding shuhong performed 70 drum ballads and drum preludes, including "Tracks in The Snowy Forest" "Ding Xiuying Waiting for Her Husband" "God of War" "Two Wives" "Family Planning is Good" "Scientific Outlook on Development Guides Us through the Voyage" "There is a Star in the Hearts of Our People", in more than 670 occasions, together with her sister Ding Lihua. Apart from the daily work of the troupe, she teaches and practices the drum in the training school of Donglu drum. She thinks that teaching and learning promotes each other mutually. She has taught 74 inheritors of Donglu drum, and contributed to passing down this treasure of folk art.

In October 2008, "There is a Star in the Hearts of Our People", which was written and performed by Ding Shuhong and her sister, gained the third prize in a provincial literal and artistic works exhibition. Also, for 13 consecutive years, Ms. Ding and her sister performed Donglu drum at the Spring Festival Gala of Anqiu. She was awarded 16 prizes at provincial, municipal and county levels and performed 76 songs.

东路大鼓传承人——周金山

周金山，男，1940 年出生，滨州市滨城区人，滨州市东路大鼓第四代传承人。

鲁北的东路大鼓独树一帜，带有鲜明的黄河三角洲的乡土气息。唱腔刚柔相济，高低相应，豪放委婉，情感细腻;表演简洁明快，主题突出;语言简练，说唱并用;道白乡土味浓厚，地方语言朴实、诙谐。

1954 年，13 岁的周金山因家庭贫困，没有读完小学就辍学了，随后跟随双目失明的父亲周胜魁赶集串乡，一为给父亲领路，二为减轻家庭负担。在听父亲说唱的过程中，周金山也学会说唱了许多书目。父亲不幸转年病逝，周金山为继承父业，又跟师伯朱胜祥习唱。从此以后，周金山就一直从事鼓书说唱。

周金山在长期的艺术实践中，形成了独特的个人艺术风格。他的嗓音好，高如鸣金，低似流水，清脆悦耳，同时也体现了鲁北东路大鼓的艺术特色。

周金山在 30 多年工作中，一直从事东路大鼓的传承工作，退休后仍然没有放弃对东路大鼓的研究和传承工作，积极培育东路大鼓下一代接班人，为滨州东路大鼓的传承和发展贡献着自己的力量。多年来，周金山多次在曲艺会演、比赛中获得荣誉。1996 年，周金山参加省首届农民文化艺术节，演唱东路大鼓《孝顺有方》获得银奖。2000 年，周金山参加山东省曲艺会演，演唱东路大鼓《二妮出嫁》获特别荣誉奖。2007 年，周金山被评为“首批滨州市优秀民间艺人”。2010~2011 年，周金山连续两年参加胡集书会都被评为“优秀演员”。

Zhou Jinshan—Inheritor of Donglu Drum

Zhou Jinshan, male, was born in 1940, in the Bincheng District, Binzhou City, Shandong Province. He is the fourth generation of inheritor of Donglu drum of Binzhou.

Donglu drum in the north of Shandong has a unique style and a distinct rural flavor of the Yellow River Delta: it couples hardness with softness, rises with falls. It can be bold, implicit and delicate; the performance is brisk and brief with a highlighted theme; its language is concise and can be spoken and sung; the spoken parts have a strong rural flavor, and the local dialect is simple and humorous.

In 1954, due to poverty, the 13-year-old Zhou Jinshan dropped out before finishing the primary school. Later, he went to markets and villages in accompany with his blind father Zhou Shengkui, to guide him and reduce the burden of the family. While listening to his father's performance, he also learned many pieces. Unfortunately, his father passed away in the next year. In order to take on his father's cause, he learned singing from Zhu Shenxiang. From then on, he has been singing, talking, and playing the drum until today.

From years of practice, he has created his own style. He has a good voice, high as a gong, low as flowing waters, which is crisp and pleasing to the ears. His performance represents at the same time the artistic characteristics of Donglu drum in the north of Shangdong.

In his career of more than 30 years, he worked to promote and pass down Donglu drum. When he retired, he didn't stop the research and the spreading work of Donglu drum, and actively taught the next generation of inheritors for the drum. He keeps contributing to the inheritance and development of Donglu drum of Binzhou. In all these years, he has won several prizes in folk drama and music performances and competitions. In 1996, he participated in the First Culture and Art Festival of Farmers. "Filial Piety in the Right Way", a piece of Donglu drum he sang at the festival, won the silver award. In 2000, he took part in the Shandong Folk Drama and Music Performance. He sang "The Wedding of Erni" and won special honour prize. In 2007, he was elected among the First Batch of Outstanding Folk Artists in Binzhou. During 2010 to 2011, he attended the Gathering of Storytellers in Huji Town and was elected an outstanding actor.

端鼓腔传承人——杨成兴

杨成兴，男，1978年出生，济宁微山人。

端鼓腔是流传于鲁西南微山湖地区的一种民间演唱艺术形式，其伴奏乐器为羊皮鞔成、四周锥以铁环的端鼓，表演者将端鼓在手中，边击鼓边演唱，故又名“端公腔”。端鼓腔的书目众多：一类是篇幅较小的段子，如《小秃闹房》《罗成算卦》等；一类是民俗性较强的中篇故事，如《刘文龙赶考》《韩湘子出家》等；还有一类是号称“十部神书”的神话传说。端鼓腔凝聚了微山湖人民的才能和智慧，保留了独具特色的湖区民间艺术及风俗。

杨成兴出生于微山县端鼓腔世家，从1984年开始跟随祖父和父亲学唱端鼓腔，基本功扎实；1990年参加演出；1996年成为端鼓腔主演；1998年成为端鼓腔领坛；现为端鼓庄户剧团团长，

杨成兴在端鼓腔表演方面有较高的天赋，能熟练地背诵几十台连台大戏的唱词和道白，伴男角粗犷豪放，韵味淳厚，行走大方；伴女角婉转优美，细腻含蓄。声音洪亮高亢，唱腔粗犷豪放、韵味淳厚，他把这种演唱特点融汇贯通于端鼓腔中，形成了憨厚质朴、刚柔兼长、丰富多变的独特艺术风格。

2007年3月，在杨成兴的努力与组织下，成立了微山县昭阳街道爱湖村端鼓腔庄户剧团，常年授徒，受到了省内外人士的好评。2003年，中央电视台对微山湖端鼓腔进行了报道，并在“走遍中国—运河文化”栏目播出。在杨成兴的积极配合下，新编端鼓腔《说唱微山湖》《渔家乐》《水乡北京紧相连》等作品曾在省、市文艺会演中获奖。其中，《说唱微山湖》在2000年12月省曲艺会演中获群文组二等奖，在2011年济宁市新创作文艺会演中获特别奖。

Yang Chengxing—Inheritor of Duangu Opera

Yang Chengxing, male, was born in 1978, in Weishan County, Jining City.

Duangu opera is a folk singing art form popular in Weishan Lake region in the southwest of Shandong. The accompaniment instrument of the opera is a drum that is made by fastening sheepskin to a iron hoop. The performer has the drum in his hand and sings as he plays the drum. That is why it's also called Duangong opera. There are numerous pieces for the opera: some are short episodes, such as "Bald Man's Wedding" "Luocheng Practices Divination"; others are mid-length folktales, such as "Liu Wenlong Goes Away to Take the Examination" "Han Xiangzi Become a Monk"; still others are myths and legends called "Ten Divine Books". The opera is where the talent and wisdom of the Weishan Lake people concentrate and it preserves the distinctive folk art and custom of the lake people.

Yang Chengxing was born in a family dedicated to Duangu opera for generations. In 1984, he began to learn the opera from his father and grandfather and had good basic skills; he began to perform in 1990 and become a main actor of the opera in 1996; in 1998 he became a leader of the opera; now he is the head of the farmers' troupe of Duangu.

Yang Chengxing has great talents for the performance of the opera and can recite the lyric and dialogue of dozens of drama series. Acting as a male character, he is bold and straightforward, simple and natural; as a female character, he is subtle, elegant and delicate. His voice is clear and high, and his singing explicit and pure. He combines these characteristics of his singing with the opera and creates his own style, which is simple and honest, and coupling alternate hardness and softness.

In March 2007, thanks to his work, the farmers' troupe of Duangu opera in Zhaoyang Street, Weishan County was founded. It taught students all these years and was well received both in and out of the province. In 2003, CCTV covered the Duangu opera of Weishan Lake and the program was released in "Travel through China—Canal Culture". With his cooperation, the new works of Duangu opera, "Talking and Singing Weishan Lake" "Happy Fisherman's Family" "The Watery Region and Beijing is Closely Connected", among others, won awards in the art performance of the municipal and provincial level. "Talking and Singing Weishan Lake" won the second prize of mass artists group in a provincial joint performance in November 2000 and special prize in the Joint Performance of New Works in Jining City in 2011.

山东琴书传承人——朱丽华

朱丽华，女，1945 年出生，山东青岛人，东路山东琴书演员。

山东琴书早期叫作“小曲子”，后因主要伴奏乐器为扬琴而有“唱扬琴”“山东扬琴”“文明扬琴”等名称。直到 1933 年，著名琴书艺人邓九如等人在天津演唱时，才将其正式定名为“山东琴书”，并沿用至今。山东琴书是曲牌体曲种中发展最为成熟完备的曲艺形式之一，其音乐形式多样，兼有联曲、主插、板式变化等形式。在发展过程中，山东琴书发展出了东路琴书、南路琴书、北路琴书三个流派，各具特色。山东琴书富有浓郁的地方特色，并对吕剧的产生、发展具有很大影响。

1959 年，朱丽华考入当时的青岛市曲艺团，拜商业兴、关云霞为师，学习了《水漫金山》《小姑贤》《老少换妻》等曲目，较为全面、扎实地掌握了东路琴书的表演艺术特色。后来，朱丽华又在常年的艺术实践中创作演唱了《云中燕》《管的好》《锔瓷盆》等曲目，排练演出了共 21 回、16 万字的长篇大书《呼延庆打擂》，并进行了唱腔设计。

朱丽华声音洪亮，唱腔优美，吐字清晰，感情真切，表演大方，刻画人物准确到位，在继承东路琴书艺术传统的同时，也形成了个人独特的艺术风格。

朱丽华从事曲艺工作几十年来，坚持演出和收徒传艺，培养了杨秀芝、徐维萍、贺长煜、赵毅民等人，为山东琴书的传承和发展做出了贡献。几十年来，朱丽华多次在演出中获得荣誉，受到好评。1975~1976 年在全国曲艺调演中，朱丽华表演的山东琴书《云中燕》《管的好》二次进京演出，获优秀演出奖；参加省曲艺调演，表演的《渡河记》获优秀演出奖；1978 年，演唱的山东琴书《新长征插曲》在青岛市首届专业文艺大赛中获演员一等奖；1981 年，演唱的山东琴书《锯瓷盆》在全国曲艺优秀节目调演中获演出二等奖。

Zhu Lihua—Inheritor of Shandong Qinshu

Zhu Lihua, female, was born in 1945 in Qindao City, Shandong Province. She is an actress of Donglu Shandong qinshu (storytelling accompanied by dulcimer).

At first, Shandong qinshu was called "Xiaoquzi". Later, as dulcimer was its principal accompaniment instrument, it was also called Chang Yangqin (Dulcimer with Singing), Shandong Yangqin (Dulcimer of Shandong) and Wenming Yangqin (Civilized Dulcimer). Its official name was fixed in 1933, when great artists, such as Jiuru Deng, performed in Tianjin and the name is still in use today. Shandong qinshu is one of the most developed and complete folk art forms among others. Its form varies, in which combined songs, intermezzos and rhythmic changes are seen. Three different schools of Shandong qinshu are developed, namely Donglu, Nanlu and Beilu, each having its own features. Shandong qinshu has a rich local flavor and has a great influence on the birth and growth of Lü opera.

In 1959, Zhu Lihua was admitted to Qingdao Troupe of Folk Arts and became a student of Shang Yexing and Guan Yunxia. She learned various plays, among which are "Water Overflows Jinshan Hill" "Sister-in-Law" "Young and Old Changing Wives". She grasped the artistic features of Donglu qinshu performance. Later, during years of practice, she created and performed "Swallow in the Cloud" "Good Management" "Repairing Porcelain Pot", etc. She rehearsed and performed in "Hu Yanqin Fighting in an Open Competition", a long work with 21 episodes and 160,000 words. She also designed the singing for it.

Her voice is clear and her singing is beautiful. She pronounces words clearly, shows emotion sincerely and portrays characters precisely. While inheriting the artistic tradition of Donglu qinshu, she creates her own unique style.

In years of artistic work, Zhu Lihua performed and taught students, such as Yang Xiuzhi, Xu Weiping, He Changyu, Zhao Yimin, etc. She has contributed a lot to the passing down and development of Shandong qinshu. For decades, she has acquired many honors through her performance, and has been well-received. In the National Folk Arts Performance from 1975 to 1976, two of her works "Swallow in the Cloud" and "Good Management" were twice performed in Beijing and gained the prize for excellent performance; her "Crossing the River" won the prize for excellent performance in a provincial performance; in 1978, her "Interlude for the New Long March", won the first prize for actors in Qingdao First Professional Literature and Art Competition; in 1981, her "Repairing Porcelain Plate" won the second prize in National Folk Arts Excellent Program Performance.

山东落子传承人——张青敏

张青敏，男，1961 年出生，山东济宁人，山东省曲艺家协会会员，济宁市优秀民间艺术家。

山东落子，又名“莲花落”，因其主要伴奏乐器为大钹、竹板，又叫“咣咣书”“荷叶吊板”，是一种源于宗教、逐渐过渡到世俗化说唱的民间曲艺形式。落子源出隋末唐初，而“山东落子”一词最早见于清道光十二年（1832 年）手抄本《赶板牌子曲、快书、岔曲、马头调各样曲》中。以其流行地域、方言、唱腔的不同，山东落子形成了“南”“北”“东”三口。其中，流传在鲁中南、鲁西南一带的南口落子最早，在清嘉庆末年就有名家刘本春出现，其后的王合玉、王教增、乔玉山、李合钧、侯教山等都是清末以来很有影响的落子艺人。

16 岁时，张青敏拜落子名家代永庆为师，学艺勤奋刻苦，又具备落子演唱天赋，尽得师传，很快就学有所成。18 岁艺成之后，他常年在鲁西南、皖北、苏北等地流动演唱，技艺特长在实践中不断提高。

张青敏的演唱风格粗犷强悍，具有浓厚的鲁西南地方特点，尤其是演唱到书中热闹当口，张青敏常将手中的大铜钹高抛两三丈，猛转身打个飞脚接住再唱，有声有色，节奏不乱，这成为他的绝活儿。他音律深厚，唱腔激越，情感丰富，气势威武，具有较强的震撼力和浓郁的地方特色，充分显示了鲁西南人民率直彪悍的性格特点，生活气息浓厚，有亲切的民间风味。

张青敏凭借其高超的演唱技艺在各种比赛中多次获奖，代表作有《夸大蒜》《三八二十三》等。2008 年 11 月，张青敏表演的山东落子《三八二十三》在纪念改革开放 30 周年首届中国农民文艺会演中获“丰收杯”。

Zhang Qingmin—Inheritor of Shandong Laozi

Zhang Qingmin, male, was born in 1961 in Jining City, Shandong Province. He is a member of the Shandong Folk Artists Association and an excellent folk artist of Jining City.

Shandong laozi is also called “Lianhualao”. As the accompaniment instruments usually are cymbals and bamboo clappers, it is also called “guangguangshu” “lotus hanging plates”. It is a form of folk art originated in religion and transited gradually to secular talking and singing. Laozi dates back to the end of the Sui Dynasty and the beginning of the Tang Dynasty. The term “laozi of Shandong” was first seen in a manuscript of a music book in 1832. Depending on the different zones, dialects and singing, Shandong Laozi was divided into 3 types: south, north, and east. The southern one, which spread through the middle and south and southwest of Shandong, is the earliest one. At the end of the reign of Jiaqing Emperor of the Qing Dynasty, it already had a famous artist Liu Benchun, followed by Wang Heyu, Wang Jiaozen, Qiao Yushan, Li Hejun and Hou Jiaoshan, etc. All of them are famous artists of Laozi that have great influence since the late Qing Dynasty.

At the age of 16, Zhang Qingmin became a student of a famous artist of Laozi, Dai Yongqin. He studied hard and had talent for Laozi. He thoroughly grasped what his teacher taught him and made a success in his study. When he finished his study at 18, he spent years singing around in the southwest of Shandong, north of Anhui and north of Jiangsu and kept bettering his skills through practice.

His singing style is rough and tough, with a distinctive local feature of the southwest of Shandong. Especially when he comes to the climax of performance, he often throws the cymbals up 6 to 10 meters high, turns around, kicks in the air, grabs the falling instrument and goes on singing. The whole vivid process is with a stable rhythm, which has become his unique skill. His tonality is profound and his singing is loud and clear, rich in emotion and full of power. It is impressive and has a distinctive local flavor, which reveals the straightforward and tough personality of people in the southwest of Shandong. It is full of vitality and has a familiar folk flavor.

Zhang Qingmin, with his excellent singing skills, has won many prizes in competitions and has representative works, such as “Praising the Garlic” “Three Times Eight Equals Twenty-Three”. In November 2008, “Three Times Eight Equals Twenty-Three” won the “Harvest Cup” in the First Farmers’ Joint Artistic Performance in Commemoration of the 30th Anniversary of Reform and Opening Up, which was held by the Ministry of Culture of PRC, the People’s Government of Suzhou and the Department of Culture of Jiangsu Province. His student Li Mingjin grasped what he taught and also achieved great success. Mr. Zhang has made great contribution to the passing down of Shandong Laozi.

山东快书传承人——高景佐

高景佐，男，1933年出生，山东莱州人，国家一级演员。

山东快书原名“武老二”,演唱者俗称“唱武老二的”，因主要演出书目为《武松传》，武松排行老二而得名。山东快书是以一个人表演一部书（《武松传》)、塑造一个形象（武松）而形成的韵诵类曲艺品种，其总体风格粗犷豪放、滑稽幽默，具有独特的审美价值。

1951年春，高景佐跟随杨派山东快书创始人杨立德先生学习山东快书。他将杨立德先生所教的表演技巧融会贯通，经常给群众表演。1958年，高景佐加入青岛市红旗歌舞团，担任山东快书演员。1959年春，为了提高自身技艺，高景佐来到北京，开始跟随高元钧先生学艺。1962年春，高景佐正式拜高元钧先生为师。之后的30多年，高景佐一直在青岛市曲艺团工作直至退休。

高景佐先后学习“杨派”“高派”，汲取两派之长，又在后来的舞台实践中从京剧、歌剧、评话等艺术中吸取营养，提升了个人演艺水平。他在舞台表演中注重突出高派山东快书的“火爆”这一基本特点，发挥自己的优势，尤其是面部喜、怒、忧、思、悲、恐、惊等表情的表现，结合手、眼、身、法、步，以人物的“情”来体现段子的内涵，深受广大观众的喜爱。

高景佐退休后，又致力于山东快书的传承工作，收徒授艺，带出了一大批基本功扎实且表演水平高的山东快书演员。高景佐几十年的舞台生涯取得了丰硕成果，受到了社会好评。1979年，高景佐被授予“青岛市劳动模范”称号；后来又先后担任山东省曲艺家协会副主席、山东省文联委员等社会职务；现任山东省曲艺家协会顾问、青岛市曲艺家协会名誉主席、中华山东快书研究会名誉会长。

Gao Jingzuo—Inheritor of Shandong Clapper Ballad

Gao Jingzuo, male, was born in 1933 in Laizhou City, Shandong Province. He is a national first-class actor.

Shandong clapper ballad is originally called "Wu Lao Er" (the second eldest of the Wu's siblings), and the singer is commonly called "the one who sings Wu Lao Er", because the major piece of its performance is "Biography of Wu Song", and he is the second eldest sibling. Shandong clapper ballad is a rhythmic type of folk art formed by one actor performing one book ("Biography of Wu Song") and depicting one character (Wu Song). Its general style is rough, bold and humorous and has unique aesthetic value.

In the spring of 1951, Gao Jingzuo became a student of the founder of Yang School of Shandong clapper ballad, Yang Lide. He mastered all the performing techniques Mr. Yang taught him and performed for the mass frequently. In 1958, he joined Qingdao Red Flag Song and Dance Troupe and became an actor of Shandong clapper ballad. In the spring of 1959, to better his skills, Mr. Gao came to Beijing and became a student of Gao Yuanjun. In the spring of 1962, he officially became a student of Mr. Gao Yuanjun. In more than 30 years that followed, he worked in the Qingdao Folk Art Troupe until he retired.

Gao Jingzuo has learned successively Yang School and Gao School clapper ballad and absorbed the merits of these two schools. Later, through his practice, he also learned from Peking opera, drama, pinghua among other art forms and improved his own performance. In his stage performance, he especially highlights a basic feature of Shandong clapper ballad—fervidity. He gives full play to his advantages, especially how to display facial expression, such as happiness, anger, worry, mediation, sadness, fear, surprise, etc. He combines the hands, eyes, body, movement and steps and expresses the content of the story through the emotion of characters, which is well received by the audience.

After his retirement, he worked to pass down the Shandong clapper ballad and taught students. He has already taught a large group of students who have acquired sound basic skills and become good performers. His career of dozens of years is fruitful and well-received. In 1979, Mr. Gao was conferred the title of "Qingdao Labor Model"; later he successively held the post of Vice-Chairman of Shandong Folk Artists Association, and member of Shandong Federation of Literature and Culture; now, he is the Consultant of Shandong Folk Artists Association, honorary chairman of Shandong Folk Artists Association, and honorary president of China Shandong Clapper Ballad Society.

评词传承人——刘延广

刘延广，男，1939年出生，山东济南人，山东评词传承人，我国著名评书表演艺术家，山东首批国家一级演员。

“评者，论也，以古事而今说，再加以评论，谓之评书。”评书因地区不同而名称各异，山东称之为“评词”，用方言述演。山东评词历史可以追溯到唐代，与僧家的讲俗、变文有渊源关系。山东评词表演形式简单，醒木一方，折扇一把，然讲古论今、敷衍故事，却悬念迭出、动人心魄，刻画人物惟妙惟肖、夹评夹议、妙趣横生。

刘延广师从两位德艺双馨的艺术家宋祥林和傅泰臣先生学艺，1959年工作于山东省齐河县曲艺队。说书长达50年，始终坚持用济南话说山东的故事，描绘山东的山川风物。过去济南话很复杂，济南南关、西关、东关、北园一带的方言都不一样。他说书用的济南话，就是将北园率直和西关幽默的语言风格融合起来，经过提炼了的济南话，能够更好地表现山东人的直率朴实和幽默感。作为山东评书的代表人，刘延广的评书在编撰和创演过程中不断汲取新时代的元素，推陈出新，追求适应时代观众审美情趣变化的创新风格。

刘延广授业于刘娟、李红梅、李忠诚等人，使得山东评词的评书技巧和艺术形式得到了传承与发展。他曾被国家新闻传媒誉为中国曲坛“评书八大家”之一，在20世纪80年代初即以《虎口夺盐》《侦察济南府》和《智擒“燕子李三”》等新作步入全国评书名家之列。

Liu Yanguang—Inheritor of Pingci

Liu Yanguang, male, was born in 1939 in Jinan, Shandong Province. He is one of the inheritors of Shandong pingci, a national famous artist of pingci. He is among the first batch of national first-class actors in Shandong, and one of the Eight Greatest Artists of Storytelling.

"To tell a story is to comment it. Storytelling is telling an old story in a contemporary way and making comments on it." Its name varies according to the regions. In Shandong, it's called "pingci" and performed in the local dialects. Shandong pingci has a long history, dating back to the Tang Dynasty. Its origin has to do with secularization and adaptation of Buddhist stories. Its form of performance is simple: the story-teller holds a gavel and a folding fan, tells the past and comments on the present. The story is told with suspense and is breathtaking. The characters are portrayed vividly with alternate comments. It is interesting and humorous.

Liu Yanguang was a student of two great masters Song Xianglin and Fu Taichen, who were excellent both in performing skills and moral integrity. In 1959, he worked in the folk arts troupe in Qihe County, Shandong Province. He performed storytelling for more than 40 years. Chang Xianglin, a famous theorist of folk arts in China, praised him as "a representative figure of the fifth great development of storytelling in China. He spread the folk arts of Jinan and the storytelling of Shandong to the whole country, a contribution that should not go unrecognized."

In his performance of storytelling for more than 50 years, Mr. Liu insisted in telling the story of Shandong in the dialect of Jinan and depicting the scenery in it. In the past, the dialect of Jinan was complicated. Four regions, namely Nanguan, Xiguan, Dongguan and Beiyuan, have different dialects. When he performs, he combines the simpleness of the dialect in Beiyuan and the humor of the dialect in Xiguan and coins an refined version of Jinan dialect, which may better express the frankness and humor of the Shandong people. As the representative figure of storytelling of Shandong, his storytelling, during the process of creation and performance, keeps absorbing elements from the new epoch, bringing forth the new through the old. He seeks a innovative style that adapts to the changing taste of the audience.

Liu Yanguang taught students such as Liu Juan, Li Hongmei, Li Zhongcheng, passing down the skills and art form of Pingci of Shandong. Mr. Liu was regarded as one of the Eight Greatest Artists of Storytelling. At the beginning of 1980s, with new works such as "Taking Salt from the Tiger's Mouth" "Scouting the Jinan Prefecture" "Capturing Li San, the Swallow in a Smart Way", he became one of the famous artists of storytelling in China.

傳承人

传统体育、游艺与杂技

Traditional Sports, Entertainment and Acrobatics

孙膑拳传承人——刘海港

刘海港，男，1971 年出生，山东安丘人，现为安丘市武术协会主席，孙膑拳第五代传人。

孙膑拳，又名“长袖拳”或“二截腿拳”，体现了孙膑兵法思想，以孙膑智慧为文化内涵，技术理论体系完整。传说孙膑拳是春秋战国时期，齐国大将孙膑为庞涓所陷受髌刑后创编的，现主要流传于济南、青岛、济宁、安丘一带。“象鼻拳”“蹒跚步”是它独有的特征。它以鸡腿、龙腰、鹰眼、猴相为形，以三截胳臂二截腿为用，拳以锥形拳（又名“象鼻拳”或“单顶拳”）为主。孙膑拳古朴雄浑，风格独特，行走出手顺达流畅，手足并进力逼四梢，结构严谨。

1988 年，刘海港拜中国孙膑拳四代传人孟宪堂为师学习孙膑拳术，同时又得到孙膑拳四代传人刘峻骧、张万福、刘振厚、王玉奎四位名家的指教；1993 年，创办安丘市孙膑拳训练基地；1995 年，在北京参加中国孙膑拳国际教练班，担任孙膑拳三十二手教练。他培训的学员来自海峡两岸及韩国、秘鲁、美国、日本等国家和地区，大大促进了孙膑拳的传播和推广。

刘海港在继承四代孙膑拳传人功夫的基础上，形成了自己独有的拳术风格：演练孙膑拳 32 手时讲究迅猛灵巧，一发连发，出手不让，猛攻速进；演练孙膑拳 64 手时强调灵活轻巧，动作快速，以攻制攻，伸缩多变；演练孙膑拳 96 手时则注重手脚并用，腾跃高蹬，猛攻猛打，虚实多变。在实战时，在战术上以“空、诓、虚、实、晃、活、巧”为主，以假动作迷惑对方，讲究侧身对敌，让对方真假难分，虚实难辨，边防边打，打防结合。

刘海港系统掌握了孙膑拳的拳理与套路技法，培训孙膑拳弟子 3000 余人。1992~1993 年，刘海港连续参加两届青岛市孙膑拳武术邀请赛，蝉联孙膑拳全能第一名。刘海港带领他的弟子多次以孙膑拳参加全国及省市级武术比赛，均获优异的成绩。

Liu Haigang—Inheritor of Sun Bin Boxing

Liu Haigang, male, was born in 1971 in Anqiu City, Shandong Province. He is currently the chairman of Anqiu Martial Art Association and the fifth-generation inheritor of Sun Bin boxing.

Also known as "Long-sleeved boxing" and "Erjietui boxing", Sun Bin boxing is guided by Sun Bin's theory on the art of war while culturally integrates with Sun Bin's wisdom, featuring a complete technical and theoretical system. Legend has it that Sun Bin boxing was invented by the Qi State general Sun Bin in the Spring and Autumn and Warring States Period after he was circumvented by Pang Juan and thus suffered from a punishment of kneecap removal. Today, Sun Bin boxing is practiced mainly in several cities in Shandong Province, including Jinan, Qingdao, Jining and Anqiu. With "Elephant Nose Boxing" and "Stagger Step" being its unique features, the martial art takes the shape of drumsticks, dragon loins, eagle eyes and monkey face. When practicing, boxers are supposed to use three sections of their arms and two sections of their legs, and their fists are cone-shaped (also known as "elephant trunk fist") for most of the time. They are also encouraged to be smooth in moving and punching, with hands and feet advancing at the same time and pushing power to the four tips of their limbs. To sum up, Sun Bin boxing is simple yet vigorous and unique in style. It is well structured and in good order.

In 1988, Liu Haigang was apprenticed to Meng Xiantang, the fourth-generation inheritor of Chinese Sun Bin boxing. Meanwhile, Mr. Liu benefited from the instruction of Liu Junxiang, Zhang Wanfu, Liu Zhenhou and Wang Yukui, the other four famous fourth-generation inheritors of Sun Bin boxing. In 1993, Mr. Liu founded the Anqiu Sun Bin Boxing Training Base; in 1995, he worked as a coach in the Chinese Sun Bin boxing international training course in Beijing, teaching 32 moves of Sun Bin boxing. By giving lessons to students from various countries and regions including China, South Korea, Peru, the United States and Japan, Liu managed to further promote and spread the traditional Chinese martial art.

Liu Haigang has developed his own unique boxing style based on the former generations of Sun Bin Boxing inheritors' technique: when practicing 32 moves of Sun Bin boxing, one should make consecutive and fierce attacks, and the key is to be quick, dexterous and unrelenting; for 64 moves of Sun Bin boxing, one should counter attack when being attacked, and the key is to keep flexible and quick; and for 96 moves of Sun Bin boxing, one should apply both hands and feet, make fierce attack and change between deceptive and real movements. In actual fights, boxers are encouraged to trick their rivals with deceptive movements, and to turn sideways to their rivals so as to make it difficult for them to distinguish deception. Besides, boxers shall attack while defending.

With his unique boxing style which integrates the theory and routine of Sun Bin boxing, Liu Haigang has given training lessons to more than 3,000 students. What's more, Liu participated in the 1992 and 1993 Qingdao Sun Bin Boxing Martial Arts Invitational Tournament, where he consecutively won the first place. Similarly, Mr. Liu's students made outstanding accomplishments in many national and provincial martial arts competitions with Sun Bin boxing following his lead.

大洪拳传承人——樊庆斌

樊庆斌，男，1958 年出生，山东郓城人，现为鲁西南大洪拳协会副主席，国家级武术裁判，全国武术协会委员。

大洪拳萌发于山东菏泽，以菏泽城西北 9 公里的朱楼李庄为核心，不仅在济宁、枣庄、聊城、德州等省内地区广为传播，而且在河南、河北、山西、安徽、江苏等地亦颇有影响。据菏泽《大洪拳拳谱》记载，该拳由明天启元年（1621 年）的李先明所创，后经明、清历代大洪拳习练者的精修细研，形成了如今内容丰富、特点鲜明、自成体系的大洪拳。该拳功架舒展大方，刚柔并济，结构严谨，注重实践。现有拳术套路、长短兵器、徒手对练、器械对练、气功点穴、暗器、擒拿、散打等近 200 种。

樊庆斌自幼酷爱武术，1968 年拜师主攻大洪拳，师从多名大洪拳大师，数次造访少林切磋演习武艺。他勤加苦练，不断钻研，用心揣摩，集各家之长，汇诸精粹，逐渐总结出大洪拳习练的技巧。1984 年，樊庆斌创办郓城宋江武校，以扎实的武术功底和丰富的学习执教经验，为发展、创新和传承大洪拳奠定坚实基础。

樊庆斌在大洪拳打法上追求有膀不见膀，无膀却有膀，手去复捺膀；在技法上强调直闯硬进，强攻中路，打里手争中门，或两厢闪击，刁打倒取之法；在战术上善于声东击西，佯攻实退，虚实兼用，乘势飞击，击其要害。他精通十八般兵器，尤擅梨花枪、蟠龙棍、春秋刀、单鞭。

由樊庆斌创办的郓城宋江武校重点传授大洪拳套路，30 年来培养武术人才 3 万余名。1995 年，樊庆斌被评选为“山东省十大杰出青年”“全国体育先进工作者”；2005 年，被评选为市级劳动模范、省二等功；2011 年，获国家“五一劳动奖章”。

Fan Qingbin—Inheritor of Dahong Boxing

Fan Qingbin, male, was born in 1958 in Yuncheng, Shandong Province. He is currently the vice chairman of the Dahong Boxing Association in Southwest Shandong, a national martial arts referee, and a member of the China National Martial Arts Association.

Originated in Heze City, Shandong Province, Dahong boxing is mainly practiced today at Zhulou Lizhuang, a village that lies nine kilometers away to the northwest of Heze City. Besides, it is also popular in other cities in Shandong including Jining, Zaozhuang, Liaocheng and Dezhou, and it has a great influence in other neighboring provinces including Henan, Hebei, Shanxi, Anhui, and Jiangsu. According to a book illustrating the martial art, Dahong boxing was created by Li Xianming in 1621. After being carefully studied and improved by practitioners in the Ming and Qing Dynasties, the martial art is now rich in contents, distinctive in features and unique in style. When practicing Dahong boxing, boxers widely stretch their bodies and sustain a balance between softness and strength. It is a practical martial art with strict structure. It now contains nearly 200 kinds of boxing routines, such as practice with long and short weapons, unarmed practice, practice with instruments, qigong, hidden weapons, capturing and free combat.

Fan Qingbin fell in love with martial arts from an early age. In 1968, he was apprenticed to many famous masters of Dahong boxing and narrowed down his focus to the martial art ever since. Besides, he paid several visits to Shaolin Temple to learn and practice martial arts. Thanks to his hard work and careful studies, Mr. Fan managed to gather the strengths of different martial schools and eventually summarized the secrets of practicing Dahong boxing. In 1984, Mr. Fan founded, with the advantage of his solid martial arts skills and rich learning and teaching experience, Yuncheng County Song Jiang Martial Arts School, laying a solid foundation for the development and improvement of Dahong boxing.

Fan Qingbin has developed his own unique style of Dahong boxing. Technically, he forcibly rushes to his rivals, storms the center part of their bodies, or strikes from both sides. Tactically, he is good at making deceptive attacks and taking advantage of the situation to straightly strike the vitals of his rivals. He is proficient in using a number of weapons, particularly pear flower spear, dragon stick, spring and autumn broadsword and single whip.

In the past 30 years, more than 30,000 martial arts students were given lessons on Dahong boxing at Yuncheng County Song Jiang Martial Arts School. In 1995, Fan was titled as "Top Ten Outstanding Youths in Shandong Province" and "National Advanced Sports Practitioner". In 2005, he was titled as municipal model worker and was honored with a second-class award by the Shandong Provincial Government. In 2011, he won the national "May Day Labor Medal".

佛汉拳传承人——李义军

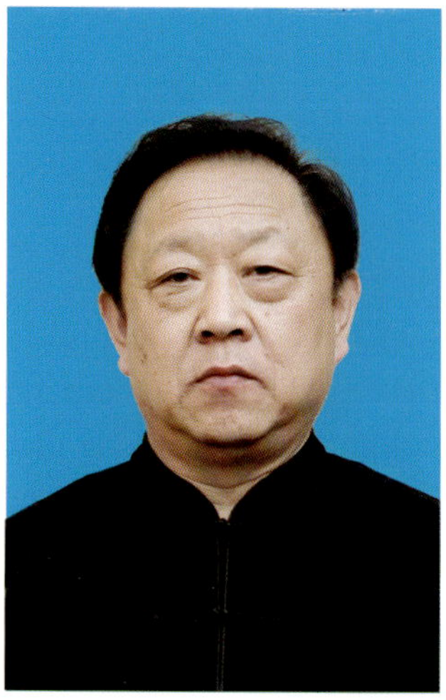

李义军，男，1955年出生，山东东明人，曾任东明县佛汉拳协会主席，东明县佛汉拳第六代传人。

东明佛汉拳，亦称“佛汉捶”。据前辈拳师口述，该拳为南北朝梁武帝大通年间天竺僧人菩提达摩所创，后由少林寺和尚徐修文在东明县一带传艺授徒。佛汉拳主要包括基本功(高低瞄)、佛汉散手单练套路、对练套路、擒拿硬功功法、拳理技法要求等。最著名的三十八路佛汉拳分上、中、下三盘，均为对打套路。佛汉拳以掌法为主，融汇了古典哲学、医学、道家太极阴阳学论等，结构严谨，动作连贯，舒展大方，朴实无华，注重实用，刚柔并济，虚实分明，周身一家，与强身健体相结合，形成了具有独特优点的拳学体系。

李义军自幼酷爱武术，从师东明县高村佛汉拳第五代宗师魏仁方、陈云汉、陈书贵学习佛汉拳。经过多年的刻苦练拳，李义军系统地掌握了佛汉拳的技巧和精髓。后又多次外出寻师访友，不断从其他拳种中博采众长、汲取营养，逐步完善自身认知，其丰富的学习经历为发展、传承佛汉拳奠定了坚实基础。

在多年的习练和研究中，李义军努力探索、勤苦磨炼、悉心钻研，对佛汉拳的套路和硬功都有较深的造诣：动作威猛刚劲，出招迅捷，精巧紧凑，敏捷灵变，步身相应，手法善变，结构严谨，刚柔相济，招法脆利，讲究佛汉拳“连绵铁”“君臣手”的优势，既保留了固有的独特运动艺术魅力，又不断开拓其艺术观赏性。

李义军致力于佛汉拳的推广和传授，培养了大批佛汉拳弟子，其弟子分布山东、河南、浙江等6省20余县，以及美国、加拿大、澳大利亚、新加坡等国家和地区。1972年，李义军代表东明县参加菏泽地区武术比赛，取得了优异的成绩。

Li Yijun—Inheritor of Buddha Boxing

Li Yijun, male, was born in 1955 in Dongming County, Shandong Province. He was the chairman of Dongming County Buddha Boxing Association and the sixth-generation inheritor of buddha boxing.

Buddha boxing, also known as "buddha pound", was created by Bodhidharma, a Tianzhu monk in Datong Period of Emperor Wu of Liang State during the Northern and Southern Dynasties, according senior buddha boxers. Later, Xu Xiuwen, a monk in Shaolin Temple gave lessons on boxing skills to students in Dongming County. Buddha boxing skills mainly include basic skills (aiming high and low), buddha free-hand single training routines, training in pair routines, skills of capturing, boxing techniques and so forth. The most famous 38-move buddha boxing is divided into upper, middle and lower sets, all of which are pair routines. Mainly based on palm strikes, buddha boxing combines classical philosophy, medicine and Taoist theory of yin and yang. It is a simple and practical martial art with a rigorous structure and coherent movements. Boxers are encouraged to widely stretch their bodies, balance between softness and strength and consider every movement as part of the whole practice. As an exercise with many health benefits, buddha boxing has become a system with its unique advantages.

Li Yijun has been a martial arts lover since he was a little child. He learned buddha boxing from Wei Renfang, Chen Yunhan and Chen Shugui, all of whom the fifth-generation masters of buddha boxing in Gao Village, Dongming County. After years of tough training, Mr. Li mastered the skills and essence of buddha boxing in a systematic manner. Later, he travelled a lot to meet some boxing masters and friends so as to gather strengths from other boxing styles and gradually increase his knowledge. His rich learning experience has laid a solid foundation for the future development and improvement of buddha boxing.

After years of though training, careful exploration, hard work and painstaking study, Li Yijun managed to obtain a better understanding in the routine and skills of buddha boxing. When practicing the martial art, he conducts strong, vigorous, quick, compact and exquisite movements. besides, he is agile and flexible, moving his body and steps correspondingly. With ever-changing boxing techniques, Mr. Li's boxing style features a rigorous structure and balance between strength and softness. He has successfully retained the inherent unique artistic charm of buddha boxing while continuously trying to make it more recreational, such as the "Lianmian Tie" (the uninterreupted iron-like gesture), and the "Junchen Shou" (a technique that embodies the hierarchy between the king and the subordinates).

Li Yijun devotes himself to the promotion and teaching of buddha boxing and has given lessons to a large number of students from more than 20 counties in 6 provinces in China such as Shandong, Henan and Zhejiang. There are also overseas students from countries such as the United States, Canada, Australia and Singapore. In 1972, Mr. Li participated in a martial arts competition in Heze on behalf of Dongming County and achieved excellent results.

梅花拳传承人——冯建武

冯建武，男，1968 年出生，山东梁山人，国家一级教练员，国家武术六段，现任梁山泊武术学校校长，梅花拳第十七代传人。

梅花拳，古称“梅花桩”，因在百余根桩阵上锻炼武功而得名，是我国比较古老的拳种之一。清乾隆年间，传统梅花拳传入梁山，受当地影响，融古老梅花拳法与梁山武功遗韵为一体，使拳种得到新的演化与发展，呈现出明显的水浒文化和梁山地域特色。该拳具有左右对称、动静结合、刚柔并济、内外兼练的演练风格。文武齐全的活动形式、梅花(桩)拳无“掌门”和能者为师的独特之处形成与其他拳种不同的基本特征。梁山梅花拳对梁山武术完整体系的建立起到重要作用。

冯建武酷爱武术，自幼随父练习梅花拳。为了使自己在梅花拳的文理武功方面进一步提高，他曾先后拜访梅拳名师，向他们学习武艺。他用了十几年的时间走遍大江南北，其丰富的学习和执教经历为传承、发展梅花拳奠定了坚实的基础。

冯建武在继承前代梅花拳传承人功夫的基础上，逐渐了解并总结出梅花拳的拳理，遵循梅花拳的功力特点及发展规律，形成自己独有的风格。他将梅花拳五势之中的“败势取胜”、梅花器械中的“风火轮”和由梅花拳与水浒武韵相融合形成的“李逵板斧功”“林冲枪”“燕青拳”等习练到了炉火纯青的境界。

冯建武积极参加省内外各级梅花拳组织举办的研讨活动，2008 年作为主要发起人之一，为首届中国梅花拳演武大会暨保护发展论坛的圆满成功做出了突出的贡献。他热衷于梅花拳的传承与传播，自 1993 年开办武术学校以来，他把传习梅花拳作为武术教学内容之一，向 2000 多学员传授了梅花拳，其中入门弟子约 500 人。

Feng Jianwu—Inheritor of Plum Blossom Boxing

Feng Jianwu, male, was born in 1968 in Liangshan County, Shandong Province. He is a national first-class coach and has obtained the sixth degree of Chinese national martial arts. He is a 17th-generation inheritor of plum blossom boxing, and currently the headmaster of Liang Shan Moor Martial Arts School.

Plum blossom boxing, as one of the oldest boxing styles in China, was known as "Plum Blossom Pillars" in ancient times as it was practiced on hundreds of pillars. During the reign of Emperor Qianlong of Qing Dynasty, the traditional plum blossom boxing was introduced to Liangshan County. The ancient plum blossom boxing was thus integrated with the legacy of Liangshan martial arts, which led to the new evolution and development in its boxing style and obvious influence of Shuihu culture and Liangshan regional characteristics were shown. Featuring left-right symmetry, the martial art is a combination of dynamic movements and stable postures and of strength and elegance. It is beneficial in both physical and psychological sense. The martial art is different from other boxing styles due to two basic reasons: firstly, it is not only a military practice but also a civil practice; secondly, there is no chief leader in plum blossom boxing and whoever capable can be a coach. Liangshan plum blossom boxing plays an important role in the establishment of the complete system of Liangshan martial arts.

As a big fan of martial arts, Feng Jianwu began practicing plum blossom boxing with his father since he was a little child. To further improve his plum blossom boxing skills, Mr. Feng spent more than ten years traveling all over the country and paid visits to famous plum boxing masters and so as to get instructions from them. His rich learning and teaching experience has laid a solid foundation for the improvement and development of plum blossom boxing.

Having mastered the plum blossom boxing skills of previous generations of inheritors, Feng Jianwu had a better understanding of the martial art and managed to find the secrets of it. He has developed his own unique style of plum blossom boxing based on its characteristics and development rules. He is perfect in his mastery of "gaining victory when about to lose", one of the five postures in plum blossom boxing, as well as of "wind-and-fire wheel", a plum blossom equipment. Besides, he is a top master in applying "Li Kui Axe Skill" "Lin Chong Spear" and "Yanqing Boxing", some of the skills that combine plum blossom boxing with Shuihu martial arts.

Feng Jianwu has been an active role in seminars organized by plum blossom boxing organizations at all levels in Shandong and other provinces. In 2008, Mr. Feng, as one of the main sponsors, made outstanding contributions to the success of the first China Plum Blossom Boxing Performance Conference and Plum Blossom Protection and Development Forum. Keen on improving and promoting plum blossom boxing, Mr. Feng integrated the martial art into his teaching schedule and has given training lessons on plum blossom boxing to more than 2,000 students (of whom about 500 were official followers) since the establishment of his martial arts school in 1993.

子午门传承人——宋义祥

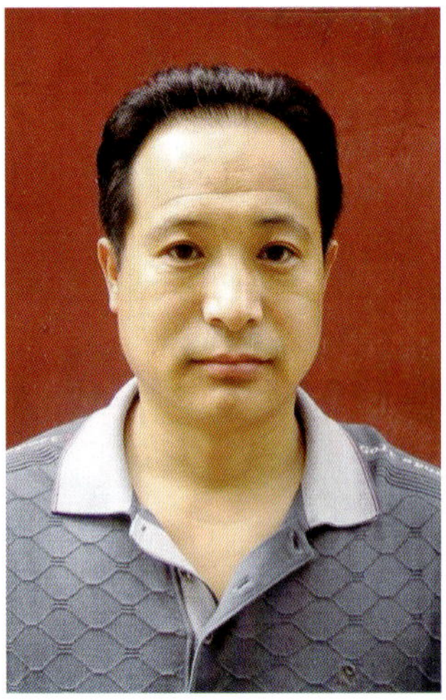

宋义祥，男，1970年出生，山东梁山人，现为子午门二十一代掌门人。

子午门是北宋末年创立的武术流派，发祥于水泊梁山一带。此功多练于子、午两个时辰，阴为子，阳为午，故名“子午门”。子午门功夫以子午拳为主体，由民间系列武术共同组成，包括武松拳、智深拳等七十二种套路和七十二种器械套路、三十六套内功功法。其技击方法一般可分为踢、打、破、摔、拿、击、刺七大类，这些方法都比较适合当时的作战方式，特别注重实用性，具有刚柔相济、内外兼修的技术特征。该拳以忠孝、尚义、诚信为主的武德，熔铸了梁山一带古朴、尚武、仁义的民风，见证着中华民族鲜活的地域传统文化特色。

宋义祥自幼酷爱武术，12岁随子午门二十代掌门人奇真大师习武。1983~1988年随师游历全国各地，与武林界朋友切磋武艺。1987年，被奇真大师指定为子午门第二十一代掌门人。1989年，宋义祥创办武术学校；1995年，创建梁山功夫研究院，并任院长和总教练；1999年，撰写《内功按摩智力教材》。丰富的学习和执教经验为宋义祥发展、传承子午门奠定了坚实的基础。

子午门功夫属于北方拳种，根据北方人身高力大、腿长臂长的生理特点，在创编时注意扬长避短，充分发挥腿的优势。宋义祥深谙子午门功夫在套路、内功、器械等方面与其他民间武术存在的巨大差别，勤加苦练腿功，钩挂点踹，飞撩劈踢，摔打推拿，在演练中与内功浑然一体，具有快准狠稳的特点。

宋义祥被评为“全国十佳武术教练”，参加全国武林精英邀请赛，获得拳术第一名。创办的“梁山功夫研究院”，先后培养武术学员10000余名，为俄罗斯、保加利亚、法国等国家和地区培养武术教练60余名。

Song Yixiang—Inheritor of Ziwumen

Song Yixiang, male, was born in 1970 in Liangshan County, Shandong Province. He is the current chief master of the 21st generation of Ziwumen inheritors.

Ziwumen, officially founded in the late Northern Song Dynasty as a martial art school, was originated near Liangshan Moor. As the martial art was usually practiced during zishi (23:00-1:00, which belongs to Yin) and wushi (11:00-13:00, which belongs to Yang), it was therefore named "Ziwumen". With Ziwu Boxing as its main content, Ziwumen consists of a series of folk martial arts, including 72 routines such as Wu Song Boxing and Zhishen Boxing, 72 instrumental routines and 36 sets of internal exercise. Generally, its attacking methods can be divided into seven categories: kicking, hitting, breaking, throwing, grabbing, striking and stabbing, which were applicable for the warfare back in Northern Song Dynasty. As a practical martial art that emphasizes the balance between strength and elegance, it is beneficial in both physical and psychological sense. Besides, Ziwumen practitioners hold the beliefs such as faithfulness, filiality, righteousness and honesty, echoing the simple, martial and righteous folkway of Liangshan region. It is a vivid symbol of the characteristics of regional and traditional culture.

As a feverish fan for martial arts, Song Yixiang started practicing kungfu with Master Qizhen, the chief leader of the 20th-generation Ziwumen inheritors when he was 12. From 1983 to 1988, he traveled all over the China with Master Qizhen to further improve his skills by communicating with other masters in martial arts field. In 1987, Song was appointed as the chief leader of the 21st-generation Ziwumen inheritors by Master Qizhen. In 1989, Mr. Song founded a martial arts school. In 1995, Liangshan Kungfu Research Institute, where Mr. Song served as president and chief coach, was established. In 1999, he wrote *A Textbook of Massage by Internal Force*. With his rich learning and teaching experience as solid foundation, Mr. Song managed to further develop and improve Ziwumen.

As Ziwumen kungfu was originated in north China where people were relatively tall and strong with long limbs, its inventors focused on fostering strengths and avoiding weaknesses of their physical features. Therefore, the advantages of their long legs were given full play. Convinced that there are great differences between Ziwumen and other folk martial arts when it comes to routine, internal force, equipment and so forth, Song Yixiang went through tough leg-skill training and became proficient in hooking kick, splitting kick, throwing and grabbing. When practicing Ziwumen, he could always make physical exercise and internal exercise as a whole and conduct quick, accurate and stable movements.

Mr. Song was honored as "Top Ten Martial Arts Coaches in China" and won the first place in boxing at the National Martial Arts Elites Invitational Tournament. What's more, over 10,000 students and 60 coaches from Russia, Bulgaria, France and Southeast Asia were trained at the Liangshan Kungfu Research Institute that he founded.

聊城杂技传承人——王峰

王峰，男，1967年出生，山东东阿人，现任聊城市杂技团常务副团长，国家二级演员。

聊城是中国杂技的发源地之一，聊城杂技历史悠久，春秋战国时期初步发展，成熟于魏晋南北朝，艺人辈出。1972年，聊城地区杂技团成立，创建的“环球飞车队”填补了山东省杂技艺术的空白。聊城杂技主要包括马戏、魔术、表演三大种别，重视腰、腿、顶功，艺术风格朴实、英武、粗犷，形成了富有齐鲁特色的杂技行业文化体系。

王峰10岁开始从事杂技表演，师从父母及近代聊城杂技艺人孟广连。1977年，进入聊城杂技团工作；1993年，被聘为二级演员。主演的节目有《口技》《高台溜冰》等，参与创作的节目有《蹦床爬竿》《肩上芭蕾》等。从演员到导演，从业务骨干到业务主管，他夜以继日地投身于聊城杂技事业发展中，为杂技艺术的创新和杂技人才的培养做出了积极的贡献。

王峰表演的杂技和创作的杂技节目具有鲜明的地方特点，注重古典美与现代美的融合。他对聊城杂技不断地深入理解和研究，把杂技技艺的新、难、奇、美、险推向了聊城杂技发展史上的又一个高峰，为繁荣新中国的杂技艺术，培养输送了大批杂技人才，深受广大群众的喜爱，为传承和发展聊城杂技奠定了坚实的基础。

王峰主演的作品《溜冰》获“山东省第一届杂技魔术创新节目比赛”技巧创新三等奖；参与创作的作品《舞叉闹海》获“2004年金狮奖第六届全国杂技比赛”铜狮奖、教师奖；主创的《肩上芭蕾》获2005年山东省第三届杂技魔术比赛一等奖。除此之外，王峰主演和创作的节目多次调京参加重大演出活动，曾作为文化使者代表政府出访日本、德国、韩国、塞班岛等国家和地区。

Wang Feng—
Inheritor of Liaocheng Acrobatics

Wang Feng, male, was born in 1967 in Dong'e County, Shandong Province. He is currently the executive deputy head of Liaocheng Acrobatics Troupe and a national second-class actor.

Originated in Liaocheng City, one of the cradles of Chinese acrobatics in the late Neolithic age, Liaocheng acrobatics went through an initial development process in the Spring and Autumn and the Warring States Periods, and became mature in the Wei Jin Southern and Northern Dynasties, boasting a long history and numerous excellent acrobats. The year of 1972 witnessed the establishment of Liaocheng Acrobatics Troupe, and the Global Acrobatic Motorcycle Team in the troupe filled the gap in acrobatic arts in Shandong Province. With circus, magic show and performance being its main content, Liaocheng Acrobatics demands that acrobats put special emphasis on using their waist, legs and doing handstand exercise. Known as a simple, heroic and straightforward acrobatic art, it is an essential part of the culture system in acrobatic industry with unique characteristics of Shandong Province.

As an apprentice to his parents and Meng Guanglian, a modern Liaocheng acrobat, Wang Feng began to perform acrobatics at the age of ten. In 1977, he joined Liaocheng Acrobatics Troupe. In 1993, he was ranked as a national second-class actor. In addition to starring in shows including "Ventriloquism" and "Roller Skating on a High Stage", Mr. Wang co-produced shows including "Climbing the Pole with the Trampoline" and "Ballet on Shoulders". By working first as an acrobat and business backbone, and later an acrobatic director and business supervisor, Mr. Wang has devoted his whole life to Liaocheng Acrobatics. He has been a great contributor for the improvement of acrobatic art and the cultivation of acrobatic professionals.

Known for their distinct local characteristics, the acrobatic shows starred and produced by Wang Feng are integrations of classical and modern beauty. By continuously doing in-depth research on the acrobatic art, Mr. Wang has managed to elevate Liaocheng Acrobatics to new heights by adding more difficult and dangerous movements to it and making it even more novel, wonderful and enjoyable. Additionally, to boom the acrobatic arts industry in China, Mr. Wang has coached a large number of acrobatic professionals, laying a solid foundation for the future improvement and development of Liaocheng Acrobatics.

The following are the prizes he won with his works: "Roller Skating" (starred by WangFeng) won the third prize for skill innovation in the First Shandong Acrobatic Magic Innovation Shows Competition; "Wucha Nao Hai" (co-produced by Wang Feng) won the Bronze Lion Award and the Teacher Award of the Sixth Golden Lion Award National Acrobatic Competition in 2004; "Ballet on Shoulders" (Wang Feng was the chief producer) won the first prize of the Third Shandong Acrobatic Magic Competition in 2005. What's more, the shows starred and produced by Mr. Wang were performed in Beijing for many times in major activities, and he visited countries and regions including Japan, Germany, South Korea and Saipan as a cultural envoy on behalf of the Chinese government.

临清肘捶传承人——申孝生

申孝生，男，1945 年出生，山东临清人，山东省传统技艺大师，临清肘捶第五代传人。

肘捶体系的形成与定型在 1874 年前后，距今已有 100 多年的传承历史。以手扶太极、足踏八卦、内劲通灵于形意为一体，兼收并蓄其他门派的精华创立而成。肘捶的基本内容由功法和理法两部分组成：功法主要有两通、十趟捶、四季捶、八方捶及天、地、人字号散手等；理法主要有玩意起名说及捶论等。肘捶运用易、医之理及兵学之理来演绎武技，内容丰富，立意精深，招法切实，见识深刻，结构严谨，极变幻之能，得自然之数，保留着中国传统武术中的原生态元素，为研究中国传统武艺提供了借鉴。

申孝生自幼习武，于 1972 年拜临清肘捶第四代传人胡世铭、张铎为师学习肘捶，后得第三代传人周子岩、师叔贾文远的教诲和指点，较全面地掌握临清肘捶的理论和技艺，为传承及教学积累了丰富的经验。

申孝生对临清肘捶的用法及变化，深刻领悟其内在价值。他灵活地运用肘捶“集百家之长，贴近实战，拳路不虚，招招制敌”的优势，勤加苦练，充分发挥其调节人体阴阳平衡，改善人体素质，增强人体功能的作用。

2010 年，申孝生参加全国第十届子午门少林民间武术争霸赛，表演临清肘捶—八方捶，获得金奖。多年来，申孝生对肘捶进行挖掘、考证，系统地整理肘捶拳谱，著有《临清肘捶技法歌诀》《临清肘捶释义》《临清潭腿源流考》《临清潭腿技法歌诀》等，2011 年完成《临清肘捶拳谱及论》第三次编修，并接受《长沙晚报》、湖南电视台、华声论坛等多家媒体的采访与报道。他培养的弟子分布于临清、深圳、长沙、安阳、平顶山、福州等地，为传承临清肘拳奠定了坚实的基础。

Shen Xiaosheng—Inheritor of Linqing Elbow Hammers

Shen Xiaosheng, male, was born in 1945 in Linqing City, Shandong Province. He is titled as Master of Traditional Techniques in Shandong Province and the fifth-generation inheritor of Linqing elbow hammers.

With a history of over 100 years, Linqing elbow hammers system was developed around 1874. Integrating the moves of "Tai Chi Hands" and "Eight Diagrams Steps", Linqing elbow hammers took the best in other schools of Chinese martial arts when it was first invented. The basic contents of the martial art consist of practice and theory. For practice, there are "Liangtong", "Shitang Hammers" "Siji Hammers" "Bafang Hammers" "Sanshou of Heaven" "Sanshou of Earth" and "Sanshou of Human", etc. For theory, there are "Theory of Naming Things" "Elbow Hammer Theory", and so on. With theory of changes, traditional Chinese medicine and art of war as theoretical support, Linqing elbow hammers is rich in content, deep in conception, practical in moves, profound in knowledge and rigorous in structure. It is an ever-changing and evolving martial art that combines with various elements in Mother Nature. There is no doubt that it is a valuable reference for the study of Chinese traditional martial arts as it retains the original ecological elements of them.

Shen Xiaosheng started practicing martial arts at an early age. In 1972, he was apprenticed to Hu Shiming and Zhang Duo, the fourth-generation inheritors of Linqing elbow hammers. Later, he was lucky enough to get instructions from Zhou Ziyan and Jia Wenyuan, the third-generation inheritors of the martial art. Through years of practicing and learning, he has had a rather comprehensive understanding of Linqing Elbow Hammers in theoretical and practical sense, which is significant for his work on inheriting and teaching the martial art.

With a thorough understanding of the usage and changes of Linqing elbow hammers, Shen Xiaosheng knows the internal value of the martial art very well. It is known for "gathering the strengths of numerous martial professionals, applicable to actual combats, and every movement is practical enough to defeat your rival". Besides, as it is said, by practicing Lingqing elbow hammers, one can balance the yin and yang elements in his body, boost his immune system and make his body function at its best. Mr. Shen has been working hard and diligently to give full play to the benefits of the martial art.

In 2010, Shen Xiaosheng won the gold medal at the Tenth National Ziwumen Shaolin Folk Martial Arts Competition by performing "Bafang Hammers". Over the years, besides numerous exploration and research on Linqing elbow hammers, Mr. Shen systematized some historical documents on the martial art and wrote such works as *Formulas of Linqing Elbow Hammers Techniques*, *Introduction to Linqing Elbow Hammers*, *Origin and Development of Linqing Tan Tui* and *Formulas of Linqing Tan Tui Techniques*. In 2011, he completed the third edition of *Theory of Linqing Elbow Hammers* and was interviewed by media such as *Changsha Evening News*, Hunan TV Station and Voice of China Forum. Besides, he has given training lessons on the martial art to students from different cities in China including Linqing, Shenzhen, Changsha, Anyang, Pingdingshan, and Fuzhou which lays a solid foundation for the improvement of Linqing elbow hammers.

蝗螂拳传承人——于永波

于永波，男，1966年出生，山东莱阳人，中国武术六段。

螳螂拳是我国著名的传统武术流派，象形拳的一种，明末清初所创，距今已有300多年的历史。螳螂拳法取螳螂捕蝉之神态，赋其阴阳、刚柔、虚实之理，施以上下、左右、前后、进退之法，演古传十八家手法于一体而创，主要在莱阳一带流传，后传至烟台、青岛等地。螳螂拳的手法主要是“勾、搂、采、挂、黏、沾，拜、贴、来、叫、顺、送”十二字诀，要求“不刁不打，刁就打，一打几下”的连环进攻。该拳具有正迎侧击、虚实相互、长短兼备、刚柔并济、手脚并用、使人难以捉摸、防不胜防的特点。练习螳螂拳，不仅可以掌握护身制敌的本领，还能提高身体素质、心理素质和道德情操。

于永波酷爱武术。1979年，跟随刘美杰老师学习螳螂拳法。长期的习武经历为于永波发展和传承螳螂拳奠定了坚实的基础。

于永波勤学苦练、善于研究，逐渐总结出螳螂拳习练的技巧：在手法方面，既有大开大合的长打手，又有短小快捷的偷漏手，既有肘靠擒拿，又有趟地摔打、连环紧扣的手法让对手无喘息机会；在套路演练方面，讲究快而不乱、刚而不僵、柔而不软，套路结构严谨，动作之间衔接巧妙。他凭借着稳健、扎实、灵活的基本功，展现了螳螂拳快速勇猛、斩钉截铁、勇往直前的气势。

于永波多次参加国际国内大型武术比赛，曾获第二届黄山论剑武术比赛螳螂拳和玉环刀一等奖；受邀在中央电视台、中国人民解放军海政文工团和山东莱阳市举办的首届梨文化节大型文艺活动上表演莱阳太极螳螂拳；受邀参加莱阳市春节晚会表演太极螳螂拳。自1989年开始授徒，共传授学生300余人。

Yu Yongbo—Inheritor of Mantis Boxing

Yu Yongbo, male, was born in 1966 in Laiyang City, Shandong Province. He has obtained the sixth degree of Chinese national martial arts.

Mantis boxing is a famous school of traditional Chinese martial art, and is an imitation boxing. It was created in the late Ming and early Qing Dynasties and enjoyed a long and rich history of more than 300 years. Mantis boxing is based on the posture of a mantis catching a cicada, endowed with the balanced combination of yin and yang, hardness and softness, nihility and existence, and equipped with the up-and-down move, left-and-right move, back-and-forth move, advance-and-retreat move. It is a fusion of 18 ancient martial art techniques. It was first well-received in Laiyang city and then spread to Yantai City, Qingdao City among other places. Its tactics are mainly "hook, hug, pick, hang, stick, paste, touch, lean, block, advance, collapse, and hit", as summarized in these 12 characters. The attacks are usually serial. "No blocking, no attacking. When blocked, attach continuously." Mantis boxing is unique in that it confronts upfront but attacks on the side, uses deceptive moves to confuse opponents, and couples long moves with short moves, hardness with softness, and hands with feet, making itself hard to predict and defend. Practicing mantis boxing can not only enhance one's self-defense capability against enemies, but also improve one's physical strength, psychological quality and moral sense.

Yu Yongbo is a devoted martial art lover. In 1979, he learned mantis boxing from Liu Meijie. The years he spent on practicing martial art has laid a solid foundation for his work of developing and passing down the tradition of northern

praying mantis.

Yu Yongbo trains extremely hard and studies mantis boxing carefully. Little by little, he summarized the practicing methods of Mantis boxing. In terms of moves, he found that there should be big bold moves as well as small sneaky moves, defending moves as well as attacking moves, and that attacks should be in close succession so that the opponent has no room to collect himself. In terms of routine practicing, it should be fast but not chaotic, firm but not rigid, soft but not weak. Every routine should be well structured and every move should be well linked with the next one. With his solid and flexible skills, he manifests the fast, forceful, decisive and unrelenting nature of mantis boxing.

In his participation in various nationwide martial art contests, Yu Yongbo won the first prizes in mantis boxing and Yuhuan sword events of the 2nd Huangshan Mountain Martial Art Contest. He was also invited to perform Mantis boxing on China Central Television, in Haizheng Art Troupe of the People's Liberation Army, and on the 1st Pear Culture Festival hosted in Laiyang as well as the Spring Festival Gala of Laiyang. In addition, he has taught about 300 students since he took on teaching in 1989.

徐家拳传承人——徐勤启

徐勤启，男，1964 年出生，山东新泰人，现为中国武术协会会员，徐家拳第十代传人。

徐家拳起源于清雍正年间，由徐氏高祖徐盛才所创，传承至第六代时，徐家拳已形成完整的体系。徐家拳主要内容体系包括拳术、拳术对练、器械、器械对练、拆手、内功、辅助功法共六类；疯魔棍、九龙棍、三节棍、春秋刀、单刀、长矛、七节鞭和羊角拐八种器械。该拳拳术和器械独具特色，在充分吸收少林、武当功夫精华的基础上，根据多年的实践经验，形成了稳、准、狠的基本特征。徐家拳高难度的技巧和独特的打法使其成为一个重要的拳种，为群众强身健体和丰富精神文化生活增添了实用性和实践性。

徐勤启自幼跟爷爷学武，十年如一日，不间断地习练徐家拳，多次访问武术名师，切磋拳术。2007 年 6 月，参加了山东省武院组织的传统武术培训班。丰富的学习经历为徐勤启传承、发展徐家拳提供了经验。

徐勤启在继承徐家拳前人功夫的基础上，努力探索、不断研究，在徐家拳中融入山东人爽快、直接、稳健的个性，充分发挥北派功夫出拳快、发力重的特点；从拳术、器械搏击到实战效果兼具南派功夫灵活、迅猛的特点，手法繁多，快捷实用。

2005 年，徐勤启获全国传统武术比赛第一名；2007 年，获山东省传统武术比赛男子 C 组拳术和单刀项目两项冠军。徐勤启在部队服役时，向官兵传授徐家拳拳术，培养武术教员 300 多名。2009 年，在清华大学表演徐家拳，在清华大学掀起了练习徐家拳的热潮。2010 年，在多所小学校园成立徐家拳培训基地，培养孩子们对徐家拳习练的热情。他大力宣传徐家拳，利用节假日培养了 1000 多名徐家拳习练者。

Xu Qinqi—Inheritor of Xujia Boxing

Xu Qinqi, male, was born in 1964 in Xintai City, Shandong Province. He is a member of the Chinese Martial Arts Association and the tenth generation inheritor of Xujia boxing.

Xujia boxing was created by Xu Shengcai in the reign of Yongzheng of the Qing Dynasty. By the time it was passed on to the sixth generation, Xujia boxing had formed a complete system. Xujia boxing mainly comprises six parts, namely boxing, boxing sparring, weapon, weapon sparring, move dismantling, internal force and auxiliary skills, along with eight weapons including Demon's stick, Jiulong stick, three-section staff, Chunqiu knife, single knife, spear, seven-section whip and claw crutch. This school of boxing is unique in its technique and weapons, and after fully absorbing the essence of Shaolin School and Wudang School, it has developed characteristics like fastness, accuracy and fierceness. Xujia boxing is an important school of boxing due to its highly-difficult moves and unique techniques, making it a suitable choice for the public to improve their physical fitness and enrich their spiritual and cultural life.

Mr. Xu started practicing martial art with his grandfather since he was only a child. For years, he has practiced Xujia boxing, visited known masters and learned from friendly combat with others. In June 2007, he enrolled in the traditional martial art training course organized by Shandong Martial Arts Colledge. His practicing and learning of Xujia boxing helps Xu develop and carry forward Qinjiaquan.

While inheriting what the past masters of Xujia boxing left behind, Mr. Xu made great efforts to further explore and study Xujia boxing. He has integrated Shandong people's frank, direct and steady personality into Xujia boxing, and given full play to the fast and heavy characteristics of the northern schools of Chinese martial arts. Meanwhile, the flexible and fierce characteristics of the southern schools are also embodied from the boxing moves, the weapon using to the real-combat effect of Xujia boxing. The moves are numerous and of various kinds, both quick and practical to employ.

In 2005, Mr. Xu won the first prize of the National Contest of Traditional Martial Arts. In 2007, he won the two championship titles in the boxing and knife section of the men's Group C in the Traditional Martial Arts Contest of Shandong Province. While serving in military, Mr. Xu taught his fellow soldiers Xujia boxing and nurtured over 300 Wushu instructors. In 2009, while performing Xujia boxing in Tsinghua University, Mr. Xu Qinqi sparked a craze for practicing Xujia boxing in Tsinghua University. In 2010, he set up a number of Xujia boxing training bases in elementary schools, with an aim to foster children's love for practicing Xujia boxing. He spared no efforts in promoting Xujia boxing and cultivated over 1,000 Xujia boxing practitioners using his weekends and holidays.

济南形意拳传承人——杨遵利

杨遵利，男，1962年出生，山东济南人，现为济南形意拳研究会会长。

济南形意拳是形意拳中的重要流派，初期可追溯到20世纪初，以稳健扎实、舒展明快、严密紧凑见长。形意拳以阴阳五行生克制化为指导思想，以五行拳、十二形拳为运动核心，将拳理、道理、医理相互贯通，达到了精、气、神与形体的高度结合与运用，充分体现了中国古典哲学中宇宙整体观和传统医学中人体整体观，具有养生上的祛病延年之功和技击上的克敌制胜之能的技艺特征。

杨遵利十几岁时师从形意拳名家高医俗、李静轩，全面学习形意拳。长期的学习经历，使其为发展、传承济南形意拳奠定了坚实的基础。

杨遵利为弘扬济南形意拳文化，同各地形意拳名家进行广泛的切磋交流。他努力探索、不断研究，掌握了形意拳“简、均、严、整、速、稳”的特点，逐渐形成了济南地区独有的风格，习练济南形意拳要以人之机体生理为依托，充分激发人体潜能，练法讲究刚柔互济。在习练和传授中，他将形意拳形神兼备、内外合一、舒展大方、朴实明快、严密紧凑、稳捷扎实、健身防身并行不悖的特点展现得淋漓尽致。

杨遵利曾多次被济南市体育局、市体育总会评为先进工作者。著有武学论文《概述非物质文化遗产济南形意拳》《中国传统武术文化形意拳》等。杨遵利积极传承济南形意拳，正式拜师入门的弟子达300余人，使济南形意拳队伍得以发展壮大；在济南设有两处固定场地传授形意拳，为广大社会人士提供强身健体、修习传统武术文化场所；在大学校园创建形意拳协会，组织形意拳比赛，举办形意拳培训班，为大学生讲演武术文化，传承济南形意拳。

Yang Zunli— Inheritor of Jinan Xingyi Boxing

Yang Zunli, male, was born in 1962 in Jinan City, Shandong Province. He is the chairman of the Jinan Xingyi Boxing Research Association.

Jinan Xingyi boxing, an important sect of Xingyi boxing, can be traced back to the early phase of the 20th Century. Its characteristics include steadiness, solidness, smoothness, rigorosity, and compactness. Adopting the mutual generation and mutual overcoming principle of the Five Elements and with the Five Elements Boxing and Twelve Elements Boxing as its core, Xingyi boxing achieves the deep combination and utilization of the spirit, soul and body of a person by interlinking boxing with ethical and medical principle. It fully embodies the holistic view of the universe as a whole which is adopted by Chinese classical philosophy and the holistic view of the human body as a whole which is adopted by Chinese traditional medicine. Jian Xingyi boxing has the health benefits of curing diseases and prolonging life as well as the function of subduing and conquering opponents.

Yang Zunli started systematically learning Xingyi boxing from masters such as Gao Yisu and Li Jingxuan when he was a teenager. Years of learning laid a solid foundation for his developing and carrying forward the tradition of Jinan Xingyi boxing.

Yang Zunli visited and exchanged views with numerous Xingyi Boxing masters across China in an effort to promote Jinan Xingyi boxing. Due to his continuous efforts in exploring and examining Xingyi boxing, he grasped its characteristics of being "simple, uniform, strict, orderly, quick and steady", and gradually forms a unique local style of Jinan. To practice Jinan Xingyi boxing, one must rely on one's physical elements and give full play to one's physical potential. When practicing, force must be coupled with flexibility. In Mr. Yang's practicing and teaching, he demonstrated the unity of the physical with the spiritual, the internal with the external, the fitness training function with the self-defense function, as well as other features of Jinan Xingyi boxing.

Yang Zunli was honored as the model worker many times by the Adiministration of Sports of Jinan and the Sports Association of Jinan City. He is the author of "Jinan Xingyi Boxing: An Intangible Cultural Heritage" "Traditional Matial Arts Culture of China—Xingyi Boxing" etc. Mr. Yang rigorously promotes Jinan Xingyi boxing and has over 300 formal disciples, greatly enlarging the number of its practitioners. He also set up two venues in Jinan for the practicing and teaching of Xingyi boxing, providing a place for the public to exercise and learn Chinese martial arts. He established clubs, hosted contests, offered training courses on various campuses and gave talks to university students in order to promote Jinan Xingyi boxing.

傳承人

传统美术

Traditional Arts

高密半印半画年画传承人——别世杰

别世杰，男，1945 年出生，山东高密人，山东省民间手工艺大师，高密市文化艺术人才。

高密半印半画年画起源于清嘉庆、道光年间，是以刻版印线稿、再进行手工填绘的一种民间画种。这一新的年画品种将杨柳青年画的长处糅进扑灰年画中，摆脱了纯手工绘制约束，大大提高了年画生产效率。高密半印半画年画制作工序复杂，一般有起稿、刻版、印衣子、打壳子、开眉眼、涮道、涮花、上色等。它在艺术特征上有独到之处：追求画面人物完整；善用隐喻象征手法；主要人物较次要人物更为突出，画面对比强烈；以少喻多，画面虚实远近清晰。

别世杰受父亲别洪彩的熏陶，从小就喜欢半印半画年画，八九岁便给父亲打下手，为以后的学习奠定了基础。1962 年，别世杰正式跟父亲学印版、涂颜色和破画修补。经过多年实践，1983 年开始从事年画的制作和绘画工作。随着经验的积累，别世杰的技艺日臻成熟，1990 年创办老泉斋画店，经营至今。

别世杰创作的半印半画年画题材广泛，有神像类、戏曲人物类、人物传说类、山鸟花卉类等。内容以喜庆、吉祥、祝福为主，突出表现了人们对美好生活的向往。作品构图饱满，布局合理。色彩设定不受手工绘画的约束，颜色以黄、红、绿、紫、毛兰为主，鲜艳明快，装饰性强。

别世杰半印半画技艺高超，多次参加比赛并获奖。1972 年，他用半印半画年画创作的《丰收日记》获东北三省第二届板画展二等奖。2009 年，在齐鲁民间艺术博览会上，他的作品《泰山》和《送福人间》获得金奖。2011 年，在中国（潍坊）第四届文化艺术展中作品《二十四孝》获银奖。别世杰在进行创作的同时不忘传承，有徒弟别金泉、邱兆和、朱文博、王宝兴等人，使高密半印半画年画这一优秀民间技艺后继有人。

Bie Shijie—Inheritor of Gaomi Half-printed Half-drawn New Year Picture

Bie Shijie, male, was born in 1945 in Gaomi City, Shandong Province. He is a master craftsman of folk handicrafts in Shandong Province and an outstanding cultural artist in Gaomi City.

The half-printed ealf-drawn new year picture of Gaomi dates back to the reigns of Jiaqing and Daoguang of the Qing Dynasty. It is a genre of folk painting that is made first with wood engraving then with manual painting. It integrates the advantages of Yangliuqing new year picture into Puhui new year picture, which greatly reduces the limit of hand painting and raises the painting efficiency. Gaomi half-printed half-drawn new year picture is produced via a complicated process which includes sketching, carving, rinsing and coloring. It has unique artistic features: pursuing the entirety of the characters in the picture; making use of metaphor and symbolism; forming strong contrast by making the main characters more prominent than other characters; making difference between near and far, clear and vague.

Under the influence of his father, Bie Shijie's love for half-printed half-drawn new year picture started when he was only a child. When he was eight or nine years old, he worked as his father's assistance, which had laid a solid foundation for his future learning. In 1962, he officially became his father's apprentice and learned skills of printing, coloring and repairing from him. After years of practice, in 1962, he started making new year pictures and paintings by himself. With the accumulation of experience, he gradually became a master in the painting of new year pictures. In 1990, he founded Laoquanzhai Painting Shop, which has stayed open till now.

The new year pictures that Bie Shijie created cover a wide range of topics, ranging from gods, theater characters and legend figures, to mountains, birds and flowers, all conveying joy, luck, blessings and people's longing for good life. His pictures are all well-composed and full of bright colors which make the pictures lively, such as yellow, red, green, purple and orchid.

Bie Shijie is highly skilled in making the pictures and has won numerous awards. In 1972, his work "Harvest Diary" won the second prize in the 2nd Printmaking Exhibition of Three Northeast Provinces of China. In 2009, his works "Taishan Mountain" and "Bless the Earth" won the first prize in the Folk Art Fair of Qilu Region. In 2011, his works "The Twenty Four Filial Exemplars" won the second prize of the 4th Culture and Art Exhibition of Weifang, China. While being a prolific artist, Mr. Bie never forgets passing the craftsmanship on. He has many disciples including Bie Jinquan, Qiu Zhaohe, Zhu Wenbo and Wang Baoxing, which ensures that the craftsmanship has its inheritors.

茌平剪纸传承人——尹秀凤

尹秀凤，女，1950 年出生，山东茌平人，曾任中国书画学会理事，茌平县民间剪纸协会、民间艺术家协会主席。

茌平剪纸历史悠久，风格多样。明朝大量移民的涌入，为茌平本土民间剪纸注入了新鲜的血液，在融会贯通中，剪纸风格趋向多元化。作品创作随心所欲、古朴灵动，既有古拙粗犷之作，又有精细隽永之品。

尹秀凤出身剪纸世家，三代传承，自幼受祖母、姑母、母亲的熏陶，得到民间艺人的口传亲授。她酷爱民间剪纸艺术，20 世纪 60 年代高中毕业后回到农村，与父老乡亲、民间艺人共同学习、切磋剪纸技艺。20 世纪 70 年代参加工作后，仍然用工作之余大部分时间进行剪纸学习与创作。为了提高剪纸技艺，尹秀凤进入山东文化艺术研究院美术创作理论研究生班深造，结业后被聘为省文化艺术研究院研究员。尹秀凤还主编了《实用民间剪纸艺术》一书，从剪纸的常见类型、题材、符号寓意、造型、制作等方面较为全面地介绍了民间剪纸的基础知识，促进了民间剪纸艺术的普及发展。

尹秀凤在学习总结前辈遗留的传统剪纸手法的基础上大胆创新，将阴刻阳雕以及双色对比的民间剪纸手法与绘画、书法等艺术有机结合。构图多用平视章法，巧妙运用点、线、面和疏密变化，剪纸作品粗犷传神，刚中有柔。

尹秀凤的剪纸作品被《人民日报》等 40 多家报刊采用，多次参加全国乃至国际大赛并获奖；先后两次在江北水城博物馆举办“尹秀凤剪纸作品展”，受到专家的好评，很多作品被多家美术馆及国际友人收藏。同时，尹秀凤致力于茌平剪纸的传承工作，在业余时间培训职工及其家属，在民间剪纸协会中带动会员切磋剪纸技艺，在课外对学生进行剪纸培训，为民间剪纸的传承做出了重要贡献。

Yin Xiufeng—Inheritor of Chiping Paper Cutting

Yin Xiufeng, female, was born in 1950 in Chiping County, Shandong Province. She was once a member of the Chinese Painter and Calligrapher Association, and served as the chairman of the Chiping Folk Papercuts Association and also the Folk Artists Association.

With a long and rich history, Chiping papercuts vary in styles. The influx of a large number of immigrants in the Ming Dynasty injected fresh blood into this art. The embracing of different cultures gradually brings diversity to the styles of Chiping papercuts, which are usually vivid and freewheeling with primitive simplicity. There are not only crude and rough papercuts but also fine and delicate ones.

Yin Xiufeng was born into a family of three-generation paper cutting practitioners. Ever since she was a kid, she learned paper cutting from watching and listening to her mother, aunt and grandmother. In 1960s, having been very passionate about paper cutting, she returned to her birthplace, a rural village, after high school graduation, to work with and learn from her fellow countrymen and local folk artists. In 1970s, after becoming a worker, she spent the majority of her spare time on the studying and creating of papercuts. To improve her skills, she attended an art creation theory class in Shandong Culture and Arts Research Institute for further education. After graduation, she was hired as a researcher in the same institute. Ms. Yin also edited the book *A Practical Guide on Folk Paper Cutting* which comprehensively introduces the basics of folk paper cutting including the common types, themes, meanings of symbols, shapes, craftsmanship among others. The book helps popularize paper cutting as a folk art.

Yin Xiufeng also made a few bold innovations on the foundation of the traditional techniques left behind by past masters. She combined the techniques of drawing and calligraphy into the techniques of traditional carving and coloring methods used in paper cutting. The papercuts are usually of flat view. The ingenious use of dots, lines and planes as well as spacing difference makes sure that the papercuts are well composed.

Her works have been included in over 40 magazines including *People's Daily* and won multiple awards at national and international contests. Two Yin Xiufeng's Works Exhibitions were held in Liaocheng City Museum. Her works were very well received and art galleries nationwide and oversea collectors bought many of her works. Meanwhile, Yin has devoted herself to passing on the traditional of paper cutting. She trained staff and families in her spare time, trained students outside the classroom, and promoted the exchange of techniques at local folk paper cutting associations. She has made important contributions to the passing on of paper cutting.

宗家庄木版年画传承人——宗成云

宗成云，男，1944年出生，青岛平度人。宗家庄木版年画第六代传承人，曾获“青岛市十大民间艺术家”称号。

宗家庄木版年画脱胎于潍坊杨家埠年画。清道光年间，宗家庄木版年画的创始人宗有明等人前去潍县杨家埠贩卖年画，因经常与年画艺人打交道，耳濡目染，便萌生了自己刻版印制年画的念头，后邀请杨家埠师傅指导制作，宗家庄便有了自己的年画生产作坊。在移植杨家埠年画的过程中，宗家庄木版年画不断改造创新。清光绪年间，宗家庄木版年画达到鼎盛，全村几乎家家都以年画生产为业，附近的荆戈庄、邵家疃、双丘、倪家庄等村也纷纷办起年画作坊。

宗家五代以印制年画为业，宗成云自幼耳濡目染，8岁即能印画，后从父师艺，掌握了兑色、印刷、刻版等祖传技艺。1997年，宗成云任宗家庄村村党支部书记时，发现村内大量历代遗存年画版外流，于是发起成立“宗家庄木版年画研究会”，自任会长，专门从事年画的保护、研究及开发工作，收集了散落在民间的年画版90余套400余块。为了使宗家庄木版年画得以继承延续，宗成云还在自家设立作坊，收徒授艺。宗成云并不是一味地传承祖辈的技艺，而是加以改良，改有光纸为宣纸，改品色颜料为国画颜料，他的做法使这一濒临灭绝的画种得以焕发新生，为宗家庄木版年画的传承发展做出了重要贡献。

近20年来，宗成云一直致力于宗家庄木版年画的保护与发展工作，并通过多个渠道、多种方式积极宣传，使宗家庄木版年画的影响力不断扩大。在他的带领下，宗家庄木版年画多次获得殊荣。2004年，获中国潍坊第三届文化艺术展示交易会暨全国木版年画金奖；2007年，获山东省非物质文化遗产精品奖。

Zong Chengyun— Inheritor of Zongjiazhuang Woodcut New Year Picture

Zong Chengyun, male, was born in 1944 in Pingdu, Qingdao, Shandong Province. He is the sixth-generation inheritor of Zongjiazhuang woodcut new year picture, and has won the title of "Qingdao Top 10 Folk Artists".

Zongjiazhuang woodcut new year picture was derived from Weifang Yangjiabu new year picture. During the reign of Daoguang Emperor of the Qing Dynasty, Zong Youming, the founder of Zongjiazhuang woodcut new year picture, went to Yangjiabu, Weixian to sell new year pictures. Owing to his frequent dealings with artists of new year picture, the idea of engraving and printing new year picture by himself occurred to Zong Youming. After that, he invited masters from Yangjiabu to give guidance, and then Zongjiazhuang had its own workshop for the production of new year pictures. In the process of imitating Yangjiabu new year picture, Zongjiazhuang woodcut new year picture has been constantly transformed and innovated. During the reign of Emperor Guangxu in the Qing Dynasty, Zongjiazhuang woodcut new year picture reached its peak. Almost every family in the village took the production of new year painting as their work. Nearby villages such as Jinggezhuang, Shaojiatuan, Shuangqiu and Nijiazhuang also set up new year picture workshops.

Five generations of Zong's family have been engaged in printing new year picture. Having been influenced by what he constantly saw and experienced since childhood, Zong Chengyun could print pictures when he was only 8 years old. Then he learned such ancestral skills as color mixing, printing and engraving from his father. In 1997, when Mr. Zong served as the Party Branch Secretary of Zongjiazhuang Village, he discovered that a large number of the remained pictures of the past generations had drained from the village, so he initiated the establishment of the Zongjiazhuang Woodcut New Year Picture Research Association, and served as the president. The association is specialized in the protection, research and development of new year pictures, and has collected more than 400 pieces, 90 sets of woodcut new year picture scattered in the folk. In order to inherit and continue Zongjiazhuang woodcut new year picture, Mr. Zong also set up workshop in his own house to receive apprenticeship and teach techniques. Mr. Zong did not blindly inherit the techniques of his ancestors, but improved them. He changed transparent glazed paper into Chinese art paper and normal pigments into Chinese painting pigments. His such practices made this endangered art form revitalized and made an important contribution to the inheritance and development of Zongjiazhuang woodcut new year picture.

Over the past 20 years, Zong Chengyun has been devoting himself to the preservation and development of Zongjiazhuang woodcut new year picture, and actively propagandized them through various channels and in various ways, so that the influence of Zongjiazhuang woodcut new year picture continues to expand. Under his leadership, Zongjiazhuang woodcut new year picture have won many honors. In 2004, Zongjiazhuang woodcut new year picture won the gold medal of the 3rd Weifang Cultural and Art Exhibition Fair & the National Woodcut New Year picture; in 2007, it won the Shandong Provincial Intangible Cultural Heritage Boutique Award.

威海剪纸传承人——王言昌

王言昌，男，1941 年出生，山东威海人，一级民间工艺美术家。

威海自唐朝开始出现祭祀用的剪纸，宋代剪纸进入百姓生活，但这一时期威海剪纸颜色尚黑，不同于其他地区的以红色为主。明清时期广泛进入百姓生活当中，进入大繁荣时期。纸斗花、簸箩花、窗花、人物造型、神话故事等剪纸作品出现，形成了构图简洁、线条流畅、寓意鲜明、粗犷简约的艺术风格。威海剪纸取材多具海洋特色，动物如龙、虾、鱼、蟹，神话故事，如“哪吒闹海”“娘娘送灯”等。

王言昌从小受母亲剪纸艺术的熏陶，喜爱剪纸。他对剪纸的学习与创作从未间断，从小跟随母亲学习剪纸，还虚心向其他剪纸艺人学习刀刻技法，使剪纸技法水平得到了很大的提高。经过长期的创作实践，王言昌推陈出新，注重题材开拓，创作出版了《王言昌剪纸连环画集》和《王言昌彩色剪纸连环画集》。

王言昌的作品构图严谨，技法多样，托物寄语，借用约定成俗的观念化形象寄托人们对美好生活的向往。王言昌常用剪和刻两种方法。剪是借助于剪刀，剪完后再把几张剪纸粘贴起来，最后对图案进行加工。刻则是先把纸张折成数叠，放在由灰和动物脂肪组成的松软的混合体上，然后用小刀慢慢刻画。王言昌的剪纸形象比原型更引人注目，运用变形、夸张的手法表现所刻对象的轮廓特征，对物象最特殊的部分作扩大、缩小、伸长、加粗、变形等处理，使形象更具特征性和艺术魅力。表现人物时，将人物的衣服上缀满花朵;描绘动物时，将动物的毛皮夸张成漩涡状，或在其身上直接添加图案，使原本普通的形象变得通透，更具美感。

王言昌一直专注于威海剪纸的挖掘和研究工作，编写了《中国威海剪纸》，为威海剪纸的发扬做出了重大贡献。除此之外，王言昌始终坚持剪纸艺术创作，多次参加各类艺术大赛，并获得多项荣誉，曾应邀到法国、英国、德国、韩国等国举办展览和进行学术交流，让更多的人感受到了威海剪纸的艺术魅力。

Wang Yanchang—Inheritor of Weihai Paper Cutting

Wang Yanchang, male, was born in 1941 in Weihai City, Shandong Province. He is a national first-class folk crafts artist.

During the Tang Dynasty, paper cutting for sacrifice emerged in Weihai. Paper cutting in the Song Dynasty came into ordinary people's life. However, in this period, the prevailing color of paper cutting in Weihai was still black, which was different from the red color in other areas. During the Ming and Qing Dynasties, paper cutting extensively entered the life of ordinary people and entered the period of great prosperity. Paper cutting works such as paper buckets, paper baskets, papercut for window decoration, papercut of characters, myths and stories have emerged, forming an artistic style with concise composition, smooth lines, clear implications and rough simplicity. The resources of Weihai paper cutting have many marine characteristics, with animals such as lobster, shrimp, fish, crab, and mythological stories, such as "Prince Nezha's Triumph Against Dragon King" and "Empress Presenting Lamp as a Gift".

Influenced by his mother's paper cutting art since childhood, Wang Yanchang loved paper cutting. He never stopped the study and creation of paper cutting. He followed his mother to learn paper cutting from an early age. He also learned knife-cutting techniques from other paper cutting artists modestly, which greatly improved his level of paper cutting techniques. After a long period of creative practice, Mr. Wang developed his own new art by weeding through the old, and focused on theme development. He created and published *Wang Yanchang Paper Cutting Comic Collection* and *Wang Yanchang Color Paper Cutting Comic Collection*.

Wang Yanchang's works are rigorous in composition, diverse in techniques. They express people's yearning for a better life through generally acknowledged conceptual images. Mr. Wang often uses cutting and engraving methods. Cutting is a technique by means of scissors. After the cuttings are finished, several pieces of paper are pasted together, and finally the pattern is processed. Engraving is to fold the paper into several folds and place it on a soft mixture of ash and animal fat, then use a knife to engrave it slowly. The images on Mr. Wang's paper cutting are even more attractive than their prototypes. He uses deformation and exaggeration means to express the contour features of the engraved objects, and treats the most special parts of the images with enlargement, reduction, elongation, thickening and deformation, so as to make the images more characteristic and full of artistic charm. When depicting figures, the figure's clothes are adorned with flowers; when depicting animals, the animal's fur is exaggerated into spiral shapes, or patterns are directly added to them, so that the originally ordinary images become more vivid and more aesthetic.

Wang Yanchang has been dedicating on the exploration and research work of Weihai paper cutting, and has compiled *Paper Cutting in Weihai, China*, which has made great contributions to the development of Weihai paper cutting. In addition, Mr. Wang has always adhered to the artistic creation of paper cutting, participated in various art contests and won many honors. He has been invited to hold exhibitions and academic exchanges in France, the U.K., Germany, South Korea and other countries, allowing more people to feel the artistic charm of Weihai paper cutting.

黄县窗染花传承人——王松生

王松生，男，1944 年出生，山东龙口人。

黄县窗染花是一种集剪纸与绘画于一体的独特民间艺术形式，起源于黄县（今龙口市），后来逐渐流布到周边县市和整个胶东地区，迄今已有 200 多年的历史。创作黄县窗染花，首先要手工剪、刻花样，常用的方法有剪刀剪和刀刻两种。剪、刻完花样后，在花样空白处用毛笔根据需要着色，一般为平涂，个别地方也可渲染。黄县窗染花形式多样，题材广泛，线条简洁，色彩鲜明，多用于装饰美化居住环境，增加节日气氛。

王松生极具观察力，自幼喜欢观察事物，琢磨人物的表情、动作、神态，并将其创作成剪纸作品。父亲见其心灵手巧，很有创作天赋，就将制作窗染花的要领传授给他。在父亲的悉心教导和自己的刻苦努力下，王松生的技艺逐渐成熟，很快就成长为闻名乡里的窗染花创作高手。自 1954 年从事窗染花以来，王松生把农闲以及业余时间充分利用，进行创作、研究，创作的作品除了部分出售以贴补家用外，多用于馈赠亲朋好友和街坊邻里。

王松生的作品题材丰富，有历史故事和人物、动物花鸟等，以古朴端雅、刀法细腻、色彩鲜艳见长，尤其擅长创作花鸟、人物等题材的窗染花作品，代表作有《蝶恋花》《花卉》等。王松生一边坚持创作，一边悉心收藏祖辈的作品。至今，创作作品 100 余件，持有其祖辈制作的黄县窗染花作品 50 余件。

Wang Songsheng—Inheritor of Huang County Window Dyeing Flower

Wang Songsheng, male, was born in 1944 in Longkou City, Shandong Province.

Huang County window dyeing flower is a unique folk art form, which integrates paper cutting and painting. It originated in Huang County (now Longkou City), and gradually spread to surrounding counties and cities and the whole Jiaodong Area. So far, it has a history of more than 200 years. Creation of Huang County window dyeing flower starts from cutting and carving the patterns, and the commonly used methods include cutting with scissors and carving with knife. After cutting and carving the pattern, the blank part of the pattern shall be colored with a Chinese brush according to the need. Usually flat painting is adopted while rendering can be applied to some parts. Being featured by various forms, extensive themes, simple lines and bright colors, Huang County window dyeing flower is mostly used to decorate and beautify the living environment and increase the festive atmosphere.

Wang Songsheng is very observant. Since childhood, he likes to observe things, ponder over the expressions, movements and demeanor of the characters and create them into papercut works. Seeing his ingenuity and creativity, his father taught him the essentials of making window dyeing flowers. In his father's careful teaching and his own hard work, Wang Songsheng's skills gradually matured, and he soon grew into a well-known window dyeing flower master. Since he was engaged in window dyeing in 1954, Mr. Wang has made full use of his slack season in farming and spare time to create and research. Most of his works are given to his relatives, friends and neighbors as gifts and some of them are sold to subsidize household.

Being rich in themes, including historical stories and characters, animals, flowers and birds, etc., Wang Songsheng's works have the characteristics such as simple and elegant style, fine carving and bright colors. Furthermore, Mr. Wang is especially good at creating window dyeing works of flowers and birds, characters and so on. His representative works are "Love of Butterfly" and "Flowers", etc. Mr. Wang insists on his creation while carefully collecting the works of his ancestors. Up to now, he has created more than 100 pieces of works and holds more than 50 pieces of Huang County window dyeing flower created by his ancestors.

滕县松枝鸟传承人——王德金

王德金，男，1934 年出生，山东滕州界河镇西西曹村人。

松枝鸟是用秫秸（高粱秸）、棉花绒、各类家禽毛及五色颜料制作成小鸟，插在松枝上而得名。松枝鸟的制作工艺复杂，分搭架子、包肚、包头、刷糊（即挂浆）、印鸟眼、画嘴、备翅子等四道大工序和十多道小工序。其规格一般分为五种，即一鸟、二鸟、三鸟、四鸟、五鸟，五鸟最大如鸽子，一鸟最小如蝈蝈。

王德金出生在西西曹村，村里家家户户制作松枝鸟，王德金受家庭和村里长辈的熏陶，从小就与松枝鸟结下了不解之缘，自幼向其堂兄王德全学习松枝鸟的制作技艺。

松枝鸟看似简单，制作起来却十分烦琐，制作工序和材料选取都有严格要求。山鸡毛颜色鲜艳逼真；水鸭毛层次细腻，色泽柔和，手感温滑；用鸡毛则需染色。因此，制作松枝鸟所用羽毛的选取会大大影响成品的等级，用山鸡最好，水鸭毛次之，鸡毛最低，但水鸭毛和山鸡毛太少，目前制作松枝鸟多用鸡毛。经过多年实践，王德金的技艺已经非常娴熟，无论是大如鸽子的五鸟还是小如蝈蝈的一鸟，都可以制作得形态各异、栩栩如生。逢年过节，大人小孩手持一枝，喜庆祥乐之感油然而生。

王德金年事已高，仍在从事松枝鸟的制作，为了不让这门手艺失传，他手把手地教同村村民制作松枝鸟，使得该技艺得以传承和发展。但随着时代发展和人们生活方式的改变，近年来滕县松枝鸟受到冷落，目前该项目处于濒危状态，急需加强保护。

Wang Dejin—
Inheritor of Teng County Pine Branch Bird

Wang Dejin, male, was born in 1934 in Xixicao Village, Jiehe Town, Tengzhou City, Shandong Province.

Pine branch bird is made from kaoliang stalk (sorghum stalks), cotton velvet, various kinds of poultry feather and five-color pigments while the birds are inserted into the pine branch. That's why it was named as pine branch bird. The complex production process of pine branch bird includes four major processes and more than ten minor processes, such as building skeleton, wrapping abdomen, wrapping head, brushing paste (coating paste), inking bird's eyes and painting bill as well as preparing the wings. It is generally divided into five specifications, namely size 1, 2, 3, 4, 5. Size 5 is the largest, which is as large as the size of pigeons; while size 1 is the smallest, which is as small as the size of grasshopper.

Wang Dejin was born in Xixicao Village where every family makes pine branch bird. Influenced by his family and the elders in the village, Wang Dejin had an indissoluble bond with pine branch bird and learnt the making skills from his elder male cousin Wang Dequan since childhood.

Pine branch bird looks simple but is very complicated to make. There are strict requirements for the making process and material selection. The pheasant feather has bright and vivid color; the teal feather has delicate layers, soft color and smooth feel; the chicken feather needs to be dyed when used. Therefore, the selection of feathers used for making pine branch bird will greatly affect the grade of finished products. The grade of products made by pheasant feather is the best, which is followed by teal feather, and chicken feather is the lowest. However, teal feather and pheasant feather are rare thus chicken feather is more commonly used in making pine branch bird at present. After years of practice, Wang Dejin has become so skilled that he can produce various lifelike shapes like size 5 as big as pigeons and size 1 as small as grasshopper. On New Year's Day or other festivals, adults and children would hold a pine branch bird in hand, creating a festive and auspicious atmosphere.

Despite his old age, Wang Dejin is still engaged in making pine branch bird. To keep this skill alive, he taught the villagers hand in hand how to make pine branch bird, allowing this skill to be inherited and developed. However, with the development of the times and the change of people's life style, pine branch bird in Teng County has been neglected in recent years. At present, the project is in an endangered state and in urgent need of strengthened protection.

鲁绣传承人——徐秀玲

徐秀玲，女，1961年出生，山东济南人。山东省工艺美术大师、山东省传统技艺大师、鲁绣艺术的代表性传承人。

鲁绣是我省一项传统而古老的艺术，作为鲁绣技艺的传承人，徐秀玲自17岁开始就职于济南刺绣总厂，从事鲁绣（发丝绣）创作，济南刺绣总厂解散后，徐秀玲成立了自己的鲁绣坊并出资带徒，面向社会公开招收学员，开办鲁绣学习班，普及鲁绣知识。徐秀玲师承赵秀芬、张桂玲、赵玉兰等艺术家，收徒5人中已有3人掌握较成熟的技艺；招收学徒50余人中涵盖了各行各业人士；曾在2008年获得“山东省杰出的20位工艺美术大师”称号，《孔子绣像》（独立绣制）《先师孔子绣像》（独立绣制）等作品先后在博览会中斩获金奖。同年，徐秀玲应邀在济南市群众艺术馆举办鲁绣公益传习班，至今已授业100余人。

鲁绣（发丝绣）工艺复杂，做工异常精细，需要运用鲁绣独特的辫绣、网绣、缀绣、接针、平针、套针和打籽等几十种针法，使用编、结、缀、钉、补贴、盘金等表现手法，根据作品所要表现的艺术效果手工施绣于蚕丝织成的底布上。绣制时针法错落有致，使画面层次丰富、立体，粗犷中见精微。徐秀玲的作品题材广泛，人物肖像、山水、鸟兽均可作为素材，其艺术灵感多来自生活，尤其擅长表现中国书画水墨效果，造就了独特的艺术风格。其代表性作品《黔娄之俦》（合作绣制）荣获中国工艺美术百花奖优秀创作一等奖，《竹林七贤图》（合作绣制）荣获中国工艺美术百花奖——珍品（金杯）奖。

徐秀玲对于鲁绣技艺的发展和传承做出了不懈努力和巨大贡献，通过在省内各大高校举办鲁绣非遗保护宣传活动吸引了大批年轻学生，参与学生多达数百余人，促进了年轻人了解鲁绣知识、传承鲁绣技艺。同时，徐秀玲还创造性地总结了增强发丝绣表现力的技法，改进其装裱工艺，攻克了历史性技术难题。

Xu Xiuling—Inheritor of Lu Embroidery

Xu Xiuling, female, was born in 1961 in Jinan City, Shandong Province. She is a master of arts and crafts in Shandong Province, a master of traditional skills in Shandong Province and a representative inheritor of Lu embroidery art.

Lu embroidery is a traditional and ancient art in Shandong Province. As an inheritor of Lu embroidery skills, Xu Xiuling worked in Jinan Embroidery Factory since she was 17 years old and engaged in Lu embroidery. Upon dissolution of Jinan Embroidery Factory, Ms. Xu set up her own Lu embroidery workshop and invested in teaching apprentices. Besides, she openly recruited students from the society, opened Lu embroidery study classes and popularized Lu embroidery knowledge. Ms. Xu learned from artists such as Zhao Xiufen, Zhang Guiling, Zhao Yulan and so on. Three of her five apprentices have mastered relatively mature skills. More than 50 apprentices have been recruited, covering people from all walks of life. She was awarded the title of "20 Outstanding Masters of Arts and Crafts in Shandong Province" in 2008 while her works such as "Embroidered Portrait of Confucius" (independently embroidered), "Embroidered Portrait of Ancestor Confucius" (independently embroidered) and other works successively won the gold medal in expos. In the same year, Ms. Xu was invited to hold a public welfare training class of Lu embroidery in Jinan Mass Art Museum. So far, more than 100 people have attended the class.

Featuring complex process and exquisite workmanship, Lu embroidery involves use of dozens of unique Lu embroidery stitches such as braid embroidery, mesh embroidery, ornament embroidery, etc. In addition, its has expression means such as braiding, knotting, ornamenting, nailing, applique and spiral of gold thread, etc. According to the artistic effect of the work, it is hand-embroidered on the base cloth woven from silk. When embroidering, the stitches are well proportioned, creating rough but subtle pictures with rich layers and stereo effect. Ms. Xu's works have extensive themes while use portraits, landscapes, birds and animals as materials. Most of her artistic inspiration comes from life. She is especially good at expressing the ink effect of Chinese painting and calligraphy, creating a unique artistic style. Her representative work "Companion of Qianlou" won the first prize for excellent creation of Hundred Flowers Awards for Arts and Crafts while "Seven Sages of the Bamboo Grove" won the Treasure Award (Golden Cup) of Hundred Flowers Awards for Arts and Crafts.

Xu Xiuling has made unremitting efforts and great contributions to the development and inheritance of Lu embroidery skills. By holding propaganda activities of Lu embroidery intangible cultural heritage protection in universities and colleges in the province, she has attracted hundreds of students to participate, which promotes young people to understand Lu embroidery knowledge and inherit Lu embroidery skills. At the same time, Xu also creatively summarized the skills to enhance the expressive force of Lu embroidery, improved its mounting process and solved the long-standing technical problems.

烟台剪纸传承人——王秀娥

王秀娥，女，1949年出生，山东莱州人。

烟台剪纸作为剪纸艺术的重要一支，历史悠久，特色鲜明。其样式多种多样，有单色剪纸、勾绘染色剪纸、拼色剪纸和衬色剪纸；题材具有朴素性、广泛性、随意性、谐音双关性等特性；整体风格表现出画面紧凑、线条挺拔流畅等特点。因地域不同，烟台剪纸的表现形式也丰富多彩，蓬莱、龙口、福山等地的剪纸多采用阴阳结合的表现方法，虚实对比强烈，粗中有细；莱州、招远的剪纸则线条纤细，小巧玲珑。

王秀娥的外祖母及母亲都是当地的剪纸艺人，自幼耳濡目染，13岁开始学习剪纸花样，40多岁形成了自己独特的艺术风格。王秀娥擅长以佛家、道家人物为题材进行创作，人物有行、立、坐、卧四势，神态分古、怪、秀、雅四种，造型饱满丰富、细致清秀，装饰性强。在几十年的时间里，王秀娥对剪纸有了很深的体悟，开始对剪纸进行研究和创作。她紧扣时代脉搏，创作了《喜迎十六大》《三个代表深入人心》《军民情魂》等作品。在挖掘民间题材的基础上，她还潜心创作了《麻姑献寿》《千手观音》《四大天王》等作品。

王秀娥的剪纸作品遍布城乡，受到众多专家的好评，其创作的千余种作品被海内外友人收藏，中央电视台等众多新闻媒体曾对其进行采访报道。2008年为迎接北京奥运会，王秀娥剪出的巨作《五百罗汉全图》被中央电视台二套节目《第一时间》进行专题报道。2010年，创作的《万佛图》《天龙十二属相》在中国迎上海世博会公益书画展活动中获金奖。此外，由于剪纸技艺高超，王秀娥经常被邀请到学校讲授剪纸技艺；同时，她也将此剪纸技艺传授给了子孙后代和街里乡亲。现在，王秀娥正在研究浆裱剪纸技术，经过反复实践，获得了成功。她准备把几十年来创作的剪纸作品用装裱技术整理出来，留给后代研究。

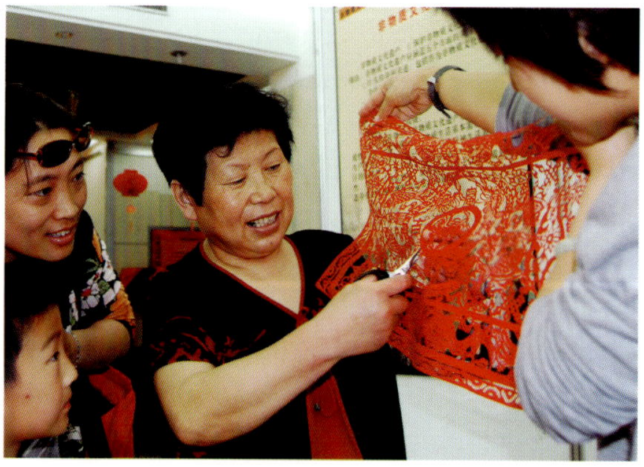

Wang Xiu'e—Inheritor of Yantai Paper Cutting

Wang Xiu'e, female, was born in 1949 in Laizhou City, Shandong Province.

As an important branch of papercut art, Yantai paper cutting has a long history and distinctive features. It has a variety of styles, including monochrome papercut, drawing dyeing papercut, color matching papercut and color foiling papercut; the theme has the characteristics like simplicity, universality, arbitrariness and homophonic pun; the overall style shows compact pictures as well as straight and smooth lines. Due to regional differences, there are various forms of expression of Yantai papercuts. Papercuts in Penglai, Longkou and Fushan, etc. mostly uses combination of Yin and Yang as expression method thus the contrast between the real and the virtual is strong while thick lines interlace with thin ones; meanwhile, papercut in Laizhou and Zhaoyuan is small and exquisite with slim lines.

Wang Xiu'e's grandmother and mother are local papercut artists. Being immersed in this atmosphere since childhood, she began to learn papercut pattern at the age of 13 and formed her unique artistic style in her 40s. Ms. Wang is good at creating works with Buddhist and Taoist figures as the theme. The characters have four postures: walking, standing, sitting and lying while their expressions are divided into ancient, strange, beautiful and elegant. The shape is rich, delicate and decorative. In decades, Ms. Wang had a deep understanding of papercut, and began to study and create papercut. She clung to the pulse of the times and created the works "Celebrate the Sixteenth National Congress" "Three Representatives Deeply Rooted among the People" and "Civil-Military Integration", etc. On the basis of exploring folk themes, she devoted herself to the creation of "Magu Congratulates on the Queen Mother's Birthday" "Thousand Hands

Guanyin" and "Four Heavenly Kings", etc.

Wang Xiu'e's papercut works have been widely distributed in urban and rural areas and have been well received by many experts. More than a thousand pieces of her works have been collected by friends at home and abroad. Ms. Wang has been interviewed and reported by CCTV and many other news media. In 2008, in order to welcome the Beijing Olympic Games, Wang cut out the huge work "A Complete Picture of Five Hundred Arhats" and was reported by CCTV-2 program "First Time". In 2010, her works "A Picture of Ten Thousand Buddhas" and "Chinese Zodiac" won the gold award in the Charity Painting and Calligraphy Exhibition of China for the Shanghai World Expo. In addition, owing to her excellent papercut skills, Ms. Wang was often invited to teach skills in schools; at the same time, she also taught this papercut skills to descendants and neighborhood folks. Now, Ms. Wang is studying the pulp-mounting papercut technology and has achieved success through repeated practice. She plans to arrange the papercut works she has created for decades with mounting technology for descendants to study.

傳承人

传统技艺

Traditional Artistry

桑皮纸制作技艺传承人——魏先明

魏先明，男，1947 年出生，山东临朐纸坊村人。

桑皮纸的制作技艺源于东汉蔡伦发明造纸术，传习历史悠久，自明初生产至今已有 600 多年的历史。桑皮纸又称“山东老纸”，是以桑树皮为原料，经泡皮、化皮、蒸皮、盘皮等几十道加工工序生产的传统手工产品。整个造纸工艺流程耗时 20 余天，全程手工操作，纸张的均匀、厚度、添加药水的分量等要领基本上就靠经验、眼力等掌握。桑皮纸的最大特点是柔嫩、防虫、拉力强、不褪色、吸水力强，主要用于书画装裱、包扎纸币、制伞、制鞭炮和文化工艺品。

据纸坊村《白氏家谱》载，魏先明十一世宗白连玉，于明洪武八年（1375 年）创立家庭作坊，至今已传承十代。

1964 年开始，魏先明在父亲开的桑皮纸作坊里从事桑皮纸生产，熟练地掌握了桑皮纸的 72 道工序。在多年实践中，魏先明的桑皮纸生产技术日益精进，于 1986 年在龙泉河畔开办机制桑皮纸加工厂，并向自己的儿子及村里的年轻人传授该项技艺。魏先明制作桑皮纸 40 余年，熟练掌握桑皮纸制作的全部手工技艺，尤其对“化瓤子”和“捞纸”两个关键制作工序有自己独到的经验技艺，制纸质量高人一筹，在纸坊一带有较高的知名度。

然而随着时代发展，人们生产生活方式发生了变化，桑皮纸需求量大大减少。1994 年，加工厂因产品销路不畅而停产，但魏先明仍对该项技艺痴心不改，四处了解桑皮纸市场信息，至今完整地保留着整个生产流程的全部工具。2008 年，在临朐县“桑皮纸制作技艺”项目的挖掘整理过程中他做了大量的宣传、示范和协调工作，为桑皮纸制作技艺的保存做出了重要贡献。

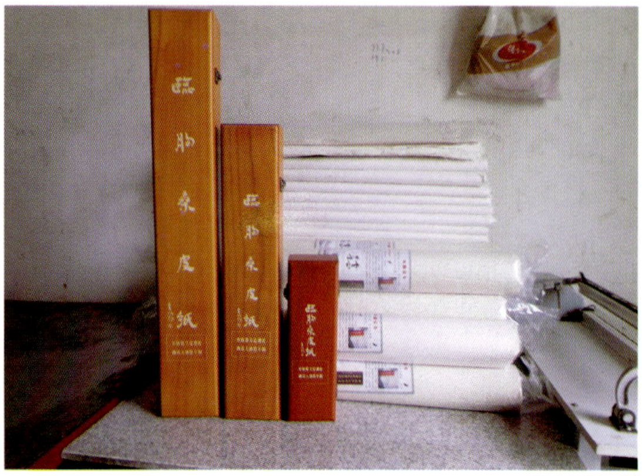

Wei Xianming—
Inheritor of Mulberry Bark Paper Making Skills

Wei Xianming, male, was born in 1947 in Zhifang Village, Linqu County, Shandong Province.

The skill of making mulberry paper originated from Cai Lun's invention of papermaking technique in the Eastern Han Dynasty, which has a history of more than 600 years since its first production in the early Ming Dynasty. Mulberry paper, also known as "old paper of Shandong", is a traditional hand-made product with mulberry bark as raw material and processed by dozens of processing processes such as soaking, peeling, steaming the bark. The whole manual papermaking process takes more than 20 days. The essentials such as uniformity and thickness of the paper and the amount of added liquid medicine are basically mastered by experience and eyesight. Mulberry paper is tender, insect-proof, fadeless, stretchable and water absorbing. It is mainly used for mounting painting and calligraphy, binding paper money, making umbrella, firecrackers and cultural arts and crafts.

According to the "Family Tree of Bai" in Zhifang Village, Bai Lianyu, the 11th ancestor of Wei Xianming, founded a family workshop in 1375 in the reign of Hongwu Emperor of the Ming Dynasty, which has been passed down for ten generations.

Since 1964, Wei Xianming has been engaged in the production of mulberry paper in the mulberry paper workshop opened by his father, and has mastered the 72 procedures of making mulberry paper skillfully. After years of practice, Mr. Wei's production technology of mulberry paper has become more and more sophisticated. In 1986, he opened a machine-made mulberry paper processing plant on the riverside of Longquan River and taught the skills to his son and young people in the village. Mr.

Wei has been making mulberry paper for more than 40 years, and he has mastered all the manual skills of making mulberry paper. What's more, he has his own unique experience and skills in the two key processes of "soaking and decomposing the mulberry bark with outer bark removed" and "picking out the mulberry paste from pool by different specifications of bamboo curtain". The quality of papermaking is superior and has a high reputation in the paper mill circle.

However, with the development of times, people's production and life styles have changed, and the demand for mulberry paper has been greatly reduced. In 1994, the processing plant stopped production due to poor sales, but Mr. Wei is still infatuated with this skill, looking around to get the mulberry paper market information. In addition, he has kept all the tools of the whole production process intact until now. In 2008, he did a lot of publicity, demonstration and coordination during the exploration and arrangement of the "Skills of Making Mulberry Paper" project in Linqu County, and made an important contribution to the preservation of the skills of making mulberry paper.

青州府花边大套传承人——卜范增

卜范增，男，1955年出生，山东青州人。高级工艺美术师、山东省传统技艺大师。

19世纪末，英籍传教士库尔德，从意大利引进一种新的编织技艺，主要生产一种用于服装边饰的带形花边。后来青州人宋传典出资创立“德昌花边庄”，开始从事“青州府花边”生意。青州府花边大套的制作源于棒槌花边制作技艺，主要是利用线与线之间的辫、绞、钩、拉形成图案，也是民间美术和民间手工艺融合发展的体现。

卜范增师从青州府花边的第二代传人王顺堂师傅，是青州府花边的第三代传人。参加工作以来，他一直从事花边系列产品的研究、设计、开发工作，通过技术创新，形成了自己独特的设计风格。卜范增所传承的青州府花边，其生产工具是十几对木质的小棒槌，一头缠线，一头系一串珠珠（起稳固和坠线作用），棒槌的多少视花边的繁简而定。常用的针法有密龙、介花、方结、稀布、双稀等，运用稀密对比、明暗交错、回旋穿插等手法，构成各种图案。图案的构成与布局既可运用对称和平衡法则，也可用连续、对比手法，以带状密龙做骨架，连以规则与不规则的底纹，遍体透空，整体具有透雕效果。绣工为一般雕平绣，布线颜色统一，绣花针路凸起，近似浮雕效果。

卜范增设计的花边大套产品曾多次获得各种奖项。1984年，设计的青州府花边大套获中国工艺美术品百花奖金杯奖；1990年，设计的青州府花边大套获《山东抽纱精品荟萃》一等奖。他通过言传身教，多次在抽纱学习班上传授技艺，并应邀先后到希腊、德国、意大利、日本等国家进行设计创作与学术交流。同时，他还带领其弟子积极参加各种社会活动，使青州府花边得到更好地传承与发扬。

Bu Fanzeng—
Inheritor of Qingzhou Lace Handicraft

Bu Fanzeng, male, was born in 1955, in Qingzhou City, Shandong Province, is a senior craftwork artisan and also a traditional craftwork master of Shandong.

In the late 19th century, Kurdish, a British missionary introduced a new knitting technique from Italy into Qingzhou to fabricate the shaped lace, which was used as the edging of the garment. Later, Song Chuandian, a Qingzhou native, invested to found the business Dechang Lace Workshop to initiate the business of the classic Qingzhou lace handicraft. The fabrication skill for the Qingzhou lace handicraft originated from the wooden club lace fabrication skill. The craftsmen plait, twist, crochet and draw the cotton thread to form various patterns. The Qingzhou lace handicraft embodies the fusion and further evolution of folk art and folk handicraft.

Bu Fanzeng is the apprentice of Wang Shuntang who is the second-generation successor of Qingzhou lace handicraft, so he is the third-generation successor. He has been specializing in the research and design of the Qingzhou lace handicraft since the start of his professional career and has formed his own design style by untiring innovation.

The fabrication tool for making Qingzhou lace handicraft is a dozen pairs of small wooden clubs, one end of which are twined with cotton thread and the other end of which are tied with a string of glass pearls (function to keep the wooden club steady and make the cotton thread fall vertically). The number of the wooden club depends on the complexity degree of the lace pattern. The popular crochet skills include Milong, Jiehua, Fangjie, Xibu and Shuangxi, to name a few. The craftsmen apply various approaches, including comparison between the sparse block and the dense block, interleaving between the exposed section and the hidden section, winding and interweaving, to shape a variety of patterns. The construction and layout of the pattern follows either symmetry & balance law or continuity & comparison law. In the course of fabrication, the craftsmen select the belt-shaped Milong as the framework which is then connected with the shades which may be both regular and irregular. The integral structure poses such an effect as openwork carving. The embroidery process mainly adopts Diaoping embroidery. The workmanship features uniform thread color and raised embroidery stitch route to present a openwork effect.

Mr. Bu had won many awards for the Qingzhou lace handicrafts designed by himself. His Qingzhou lace handicrafts won the gold cup in the Hundred Flower Award Competition for Chinese Arts and Crafts in 1984; his Qingzhou lace handicrafts brought him the first prize in the Fair of Collection of Fine Goods of Shandong Drawnwork in 1990. He used to teach the fabrication process in various drawnwork study classes. Further more, he was also invited to Greece, Germany, Italy, Japan and other countries for design, creation and academic exchange. Meanwhile, he often leads his apprentices to zealously take part in a variety of social activities to popularize and propagate this unique Shandong regional culture.

曹县戏文纸扎传承人——张于周

张于周，男，1961年出生，山东曹县楼庄乡王堂村人。

曹县纸扎，又称“扎作”“糊纸”“彩糊”等，是在祭祀及丧俗活动中焚烧的纸制品。它以草木为骨，彩纸为服，泥模制头、折剪并用，点染传神。在曹县历史上，不同时期纸扎的称谓及用途不尽相同。据史料记载，供奉纸扎的形成，是由原始社会以来墓葬殉葬俑演变和发展而来的。纸的出现使纸扎艺术的普及成为可能，至宋代丧俗纸扎已有专门经营的行业。明清之际，纸扎成为丧俗和鬼节的主要内容，工艺之精湛已远远地超过宋元，应用也更广泛，成为当时各个阶层的丧俗和祭奠活动的主要内容。

张于周自幼随父学习戏文纸扎技艺，为子承父业的家族式传承。他扎制的纸扎中尤以戏文纸扎最具特色，更注重对表现对象的展示和祭祀场面的烘托。张于周的戏文纸扎作品头部施彩，人物形象眉清目秀，非常写实。身段衣袖鞋靴齐全，强调人物动作，整体形象传神，加之彩纸的巧妙搭配，局部彩绘或装饰金银饰片，光彩夺目，艺术效果艳而不俗。张于周的戏文纸扎，往往二三人物一组，人物形象之间彼此关照，前后呼应，再现了戏曲舞台上的经典场景。戏文纸扎与民俗、丧葬文化、宗教信仰等有着密切的关系，祭祀丧俗的戏文纸扎艺术所承载的文化中包含了中华民族特有的民俗“文化基因”，是中国特有的文化现象。

2008年，张于周获得了“曹县民间手工技艺大师”称号。然而由于现代生活方式的转换，特别是传统丧俗意识的淡化，戏文纸扎作为传统丧俗祭祀的功能已逐渐消退，其生存空间仅限于一些相对偏远、封闭的农村。一些手艺精湛的戏文纸扎艺人因年龄、身体等原因，逐渐淡出“舞台”，戏文纸扎的扎制技法难以得以传承，这门优秀的传统民间手工技艺面临青黄不接的窘境。

Zhang Yuzhou—Inheritor of Cao County Opera Paper Effigy

Zhang Yuzhou, male, was born in 1961, in Wangtang Village, Louzhuang Town, Cao County, Shandong Province.

Cao County Opera Paper Effigy is a kind of paper product which would be burnt at the sacrifice ceremony and the funeral activity. First of all, the handicraftsman makes a grass or wooden framework, and then, the paper of various colors would be pasted to the framework surface to form the figure's dress. Meanwhile, the handicraftsman uses a mud mold to make the figure's head. The use of skills such as folding, cutting and painting makes the works vivid and life like. The name of the paper effigy differs in the different stages of the history of Cao County. As disclosed by the historical materials, the paper effigy was derived and evolved from the tomb sacrificial figures originated from the primitive society. The invention of the paper made it possible to popularize the paper effigy art. In the Song Dynasty, the paper effigy art had been developed into a special business industry. In the Ming and Qing Dynasties, the paper effigy played a leading role in the funeral ceremony and the spirit festival. Its exquisite craft dwarfed the counterpart in the Song Dynasty. Meanwhile, the paper effigy also had wider application and became the main content of the funeral activity and the sacrifice ceremony of all social strata.

Since his childhood, Zhang Yuzhou followed his father to learn the paper effigy handicraft. It is a typical Chinese family inheritance which means the son has right to inherit his father's cause. He is especially good at making the opera paper effigy. His works focus on the display of the figures and the sacrifice scene. The head of the opera paper effigy fabricated by Mr. Zhang is painted with various colors. The figure features bright eyes and graceful eyebrows and appears especially realistic. The figure is neatly dressed and in true-to-life action. The artful coordination of the color papers, color painting and gold and silver jewelry dazzles the eyes for its brightness but not lowers artistic effects. Another characteristic of his works is that two or three figures are grouped and these figures interact and echo to show a classic opera scenario at the stage. The opera paper effigy has a close relation with folk customs, funeral culture and religions. As a China-specific cultural phenomenon, the opera paper effigy which serves the funeral activity and sacrifice ceremony carries the specific folk culture gene of the Chinese nation.

In 2008, Zhang Yuzhou was granted the title of Folk Handicraft Master in Cao County. However, the modern life style directly impacts on and weakens the traditional consciousness of funeral culture so that the function of the opera paper effigy to play a vital role at the traditional funeral activity and sacrifice ceremony is being faded. Its nowadays survival space is only limited to some relatively remote and closed countryside. Because some veterans are exiting their "stage" due to age and physical reason and so on, the inheritance of the fabrication skills of the opera paper effigy is exposed to the threat of termination so that the once brilliant opera paper effigy handicraft is facing an awkward situation of temporary shortage.

蓝印花布印染技艺传承人——耿延祯

耿延祯，男，1947 年出生，山东博兴人。

蓝印花布是传统的镂空版白浆防染印花，又称靛蓝花布，俗称“药斑布”“浇花布”，起源于秦汉，迄今已有 1300 余年的历史。唐宋时期，蓝印花布已非常兴盛。明清之际，已普遍流行于民间。现代所见蓝印花布的样式，多数为明清时期的作品。蓝印花布色调清新明快，图案淳朴艳丽，图案有的取材于百姓喜闻乐见的民间故事、戏曲人物，有的则是由鸟兽鱼虫和花卉果藏等组成的吉祥纹样，具有浓郁的乡土气息和民族风情。

耿延祯出身于蓝印花布世家，他自幼向父辈学习蓝印花布制版与印染技艺，从事蓝印花布和彩印花布制版、印染与销售已 40 多年。

蓝印花布制作技艺在滨州、博兴一代有着悠久的历史，是一门融生活与艺术于一体的技艺。蓝印花布制作技艺的传承采取代代相传、言传身教的方式，到耿延祯，蓝印花布制作技艺已传承至第四代，其技艺日臻成熟，并逐渐发扬光大。耿延祯融绘画、刻纸、印染于一体，从图样设计、制版到印染全过程都由自己操作。耿延祯制作的蓝印花布，色彩主要运用蓝、白二色，具有清新明快、纯真朴素的艺术特点。为了使这项技艺传承下去，耿延祯一直在培养接班人，为蓝印花布印染技艺的保护与传承做着不懈努力。

耿延祯的作品多次在国家级、省级非物质文化遗产展览中获奖，并在 1996 年由山东省文学艺术界联合会、山东工艺美术学院主办的“山东省民间工艺品博览会”评奖中获得二等奖；2011 年 10 月，耿延祯凭借《蓝印花布包袱》荣获全国首届非物质文化遗产交易博览会铜奖。耿延祯被授予“滨州市优秀民间艺人”称号。

Geng Yanzhen—Inheritor of Printing and Dyeing of Blue Calico

Geng Yanzhen, male, was born in 1947 in Beiguan Village, Boxing County, Binzhou City, Shandong Province.

Blue calico, also called indigo calico, is a kind of traditional openwork printing and dyeing handicraft. It dates back to the Qin and Han Dynasties and has a history more than 1300 years. During the Tang and Song Dynasties, the blue calico began to gain popularity. During the Ming and Qing Dynasties, the general public universally used the blue calico. Most of the styles of the contemporary blue calico products are the copies of the works made during the Ming and Qing Dynasties. The blue calico features fresh and bright color and simple but gorgeous pattern. Some patterns record folktales or opera characters which are well known and favored by the public, and some patterns are composed of birds, beasts, insects, fishes, flowers and fruits, with a kind of strong rustic flavor and national style.

Geng Yanzhen was born in a family noted for blue calico fabrication. Since his childhood, the elders of his family taught him the process about plate making, printing and dyeing of blue calicao. By now, he has contributed himself into the industry for forty-odd years.

The fabrication technique of the blue calico has a long history at Boxing County and its neighbourhood. It is a technique that integrates life and art. The inheritance of the fabrication technique features family inheritance and personal demonstration plus verbal instruction. Mr. Geng is a fourth-generation successor. The fabrication technique is becoming more and more improved and gradually moving to its new peak. As an all-rounder, Mr. Geng is good at all the skills including drawing, paper engraving and dyeing. Moreover, Mr. Geng always undertakes the whole process from pattern designing, plate making to dyeing by himself. The blue calico fabricated by Mr. Geng mainly applies two colors—blue and white, and appears to be fresh and simple. In order to protect and pass the technique down, Mr. Geng has been trying his best to cultivate the next generation of successors.

The works fabricated by Geng were awarded time and again in the national- and provincial-grade intangible cultural heritage fairs; in 1996, his works received the second prize in the Shandong Folk Art Work Fair held by Shandong Federation of Literary and Art Circles and Shandong University of Art & Design; in October 2011, Mr. Geng was granted with the bronze prize for his work "Blue Calico Cloth-wrappers" in the First Session of National Intangible Cultural Heritage Trade Fairs. Based on his exquisite skills and grand professional reputation, he was conferred with the title of "Outstanding Folk Artisan of Binzhou".

蓝印花布印染技艺传承人——杜宗环

杜宗环，男，1943年出生，山东嘉祥县仲山乡狼山屯村人。

蓝印花布是用简单、原始的蓝、白两色创造的一个自然淳朴、千变万化的蓝白艺术世界。因其纹样图案的选材都来自民间，所以也反映了百姓朴实的审美情趣和价值取向。

杜宗环外祖父高西光家族世代从事蓝印花布印染工作。1966年，杜宗环跟随外祖父在狼山屯村大队染坊工作，学习染布和蓝印花布印染技艺。在学习过程中，他善于观察，用心思索，很快就熟练掌握了各项技艺。经过几年的锻炼，他的印染技艺不断提高，工艺日趋精湛，图案清晰饱满，得到周围乡村群众的认可与赞誉。高西光去世后，杜宗环接任大队染坊师傅，并于1980年开设了杜氏染坊。

多年来，杜宗环坚持从事蓝印花布印染，对印染工艺进行改进。他使用豆腐、石灰、鸡蛋清调制印染浆，使其阴干后出现绽裂的纹路，入染后就留下很多不规则细纹，纹路自然、古朴，具有一种朴素美。他的作品工艺精湛，印染细腻，色调清雅，图案内容大多取材于飞禽走兽、花草虫鱼与神话传说，并运用明显的象征、比喻、谐音等手段，使印染成品具有美好的寓意。其代表性作品有《凤啄牡丹》《狮子滚绣球》《鲤鱼闹莲》《宝葫芦》等。

2007年，杜宗环的作品参加山东省非物质文化遗产保护成果展，获优秀奖。杜宗环从事蓝印花布印染工作期间，不仅对印染工艺进行了改进，还教授了许多艺人，为该技艺的保护和传承做出了重要贡献。

Du Zonghuan—Inheritor of Printing and Dyeing of Blue Calico

Du Zonghuan, male, was born in 1943, in Langshantun Village, Zhongshan Town, Jiaxiang County, Shandong Province.

The blue calico could give a natural, pure and daedal art world shaped with its original and simple blue and white. Because the content of the pattern design of the blue calico has close relation with the folk life, it really reflects the unadorned aesthetic interest and value orientation of the common people.

The family of Gao Xiguang who was the maternal grandfather of Du Zonghuan, had been engaged in the dyeing industry of blue calico for generations. In 1966, Mr. Du worked as a trainee at the village dyeing workshop with his maternal grandfather. Due to his careful observation and purposive thinking, he quickly understood and mastered the blue calico dyeing techniques. Later, after several years of practices, his skills were greatly improved and continually upgraded, which assured the pattern design in his works were clear and rich. After Gao Xiguang died, Mr. Du became the master of the brigade's dyehouse. In 1980, Mr. Du established his own business—Du's Dyehouse.

Du Zonghuan has been devoting himself to the career of blue calico dyeing for years. He positively and continually improved the traditional dyeing process. For example, he used tofu, lime and egg white to make an patented printing paste which could form many flaw-shaped pattern paths after the cloth had become dry after placement in the shade for a certain period of time. After dyeing is completed, there would be many irregular fine pattern paths left on the cloth, which are natural and quaint to show a kind of chaste beauty. His works feature exquisite artisanship, fine dyeing and elegant color. The patterns in most blue calicoes were drawn from fowls and beasts, flowers and plants, insects and fishes, and myth and legend. In addition, the art means, including symbolization, comparison and euphony, were used to make the products carry good wish. His classic works include "Phoenix Pecking Peony" "Lion Playing Silk-ball" "Carp Frolicking on Lotus" and "Treasure Gourd".

In 2007, the works fabricated by Du Zonghuan were displayed at the Shandong Achievement Exhibition for Protection of Intangible Cultural Heritage and conferred with the excellence award. In his whole professional career, Mr. Du has not only improved greatly the dyeing process bus also trained and cultivated many promising handicraftsmen, which is a great contribution to the inheritance and protection of the precious culture heritage.

彩印花布印染技艺传承人——李景春

李景春，男，1955年出生，山东嘉祥县马村镇李庄村人。

彩印花布是在一般蓝色之外还加有其他色彩图案的印花布，俗称“花袱子”。在山东省很多地方的民间风俗中，姑娘结婚时包裹陪嫁衣被、箱柜并捆扎抬送到婆家的彩印大包袱就是彩印花布。印染花布在山东有着悠久的历史，包括蓝底白印花布、扎染花布和彩印花布三种，其中以彩印花布尤为突出，分布范围遍及省内。彩印花布的图案多取材于吉祥的民间故事和历史传说，色彩新鲜、热烈，富有装饰性，是农村嫁娶、祝寿等喜庆场合必不可少的装饰品。

李景春从小受到祖父和父亲的熏陶，年少随父亲学习彩印花布印染技艺，3年后就能够独立印制花布，17岁时因印制的花布图案美观、技艺精巧而远近闻名、家喻户晓。

李景春印制的包袱带有底色，图案清秀典雅、明快清晰。将一个包袱的正、反两面印制成不同的图案，更是他的绝活。他在颜料里面掺白矾或石灰，有时掺以蛋清或豆腐，以保持颜色的明亮。他采用传统手工技艺，完全以手工镂刻油纸版和制作刻板工具；在色彩上运用浓厚的民俗色彩，渲染欢乐喜庆的气氛；图案精美，多取材于蕴含祥瑞喜庆之意的传说故事。其代表作品有《凤凰穿牡丹》《鲤鱼跳龙门》《喜鹊闹梅》《和平鸽》等。

1989年，李景春参加在京举办的首届民间工艺展览，印花包袱《狮子滚绣球》获优秀奖，此后又在法国博览会上获一等奖；2006~2007年，他参加山东省非物质文化遗产保护成果展，获优秀奖。虽然受现代印染材料和技术的冲击，彩印花布市场逐渐萎缩，但李景春依然坚守着彩印花布的传统技艺，为该技艺的保护和传承进行着不懈努力。

Li Jingchun— Inheritor of Printing and Dyeing of Colored Calico

Li Jingchun, male, was born in 1955, in Lizhuang Village, Machun Town, Jiaxiang County, Shandong Province.

The colored calico is a calico with patterns which are applied with various colors besides the common blue, generally known as "Hua Fu Zi". As required by the folk customs at many places in Shandong, the colored calico shall be used to pack the dowries of a bride, including clothes, quilt, case and cabinet. The printing and dyeing cloth has a long history in Shandong, including three specific items, e.g. blue and white calico, bandhnu calico and colored calico. Among the above three, the color calicoed is most prominent and very popular across the whole territory of Shandong Province. Its pattern is usually about favonian folktales and well-known historical legends. The colored calico is the essential adornment in the wedding ceremony and the birthday party of the elders and other festive ceremonies for its vivid and beautiful colors.

When he was a child, he just witnessed the work of his father and grandpa. Later, he followed his father to learn colored calico dyeing technique. After three years, he could independently operate the process. By his age of 17, he had become well-known for his works which were highlighted by fancy design and finished workmanship.

The colored calico fabricated by Li Jingchun is always painted with base color, making the pattern pretty, elegant, bright and clear. His exclusive skill is to make different patterns at the front and back of a color calico. He mixes alum or limestone into the pigments or sometimes egg white or tofu into the pigments to maintain the color bright. He insistson the traditional process, carving the oilpaper templet and making the tools for plate engraving by complete handwork; he stresses the color application shall highlight the profound folk custom and play up the happy and joyous atmosphere; the pattern of his works mainly comes from some legends which always carry the meaning of luck, happiness and propitious omen. His classic works include "Phoenix on Peony Cluster" "Carp Jumping over Dam" "Magpie Frolicking on Plum Blossom" and "Peace Pigeon", to name a few.

In 1989, Li Jingchun was invited to The First Folk Arts and Crafts Fair conducted in Beijing which was jointly initiated and organized by the organizations from all over China. In this fair, his work "Lion Playing Silk-ball" was granted with the excellence award. Later, the same work was conferred with the first prize in an international exhibition held in France. His works in succession received the excellence award in Shandong Achievement Exhibition for Protection of Intangible Cultural Heritage launched respectively in 2006 and 2007. Though the violent impact from modern dyeing material and technology is squeezing the survival space of the traditional color calico, Mr. Li still insists on the traditional technique of printing and dyeing colored calico and contributes to inheriting and protecting the traditional folk art.

潍坊嵌银漆器传承人——陈增

陈增，男，1945 年出生，潍坊人，潍坊嵌银漆器传承人。

清朝年间，潍县的铜业首饰工匠就运用古代器物的金属细工装饰技法，尝试在铜器具上镶嵌金银纹饰。后来，铜匠艺人在木质的小型器物上试验镶嵌金银丝。再后来经过发展，潍坊的嵌银漆器以贵重硬木（主要是红木）为主要原料，在红木中嵌入银丝，名贵典雅，雍容璀璨。

陈增在幼年时代就喜欢绘画，对潍坊的传统工艺美术尤其是嵌银髹漆技艺甚是喜爱。1960 年，陈增参加工作，当即拜潍坊嵌银髹漆技艺第四代传承人郭玉春、陈开勋为师，系统地学习木工、雕刻、嵌银、大漆技艺。在师傅的悉心培养和自己的不懈努力下，他熟练地掌握了整套工艺流程，积累了丰富的经验。在前人的基础上，继承发展，开拓创新，做到了雕刻与嵌银完美结合。

在雕刻方面，陈增将中国传统技术与西方洋花产品相结合，不断创新，实现了中、西产品造型和技艺上的完美结合；在嵌银方面，充分采用古代的花鸟人物和各种吉祥图案，运用白描的方法绘制图案，使每件产品既新颖又不失传统风格。与他人不同的是，陈增集木工、雕刻、嵌银、大漆各项工艺于一身，不但精于动手操作，而且其设计创作的产品也达到了潍坊嵌银髹漆技艺的新境界。

陈增不仅保持自身创新活力，努力提高自己嵌银髹漆技艺，还时刻关注着潍坊嵌银髹漆技艺的创新发展和传承人的培养，相继培养了很多传人，他们设计创作的产品多次获奖，在潍坊嵌银漆器行业中发挥着重要作用。多年来，陈增凭借精湛的技艺赢得了不少荣誉。1986年，设计制作的套三烟具被山东省工艺美术展览会评为一等奖。1989 年，为北京人民大会堂山东厅创作落地屏《春潮图》。1995 年，陈增被授予山东省“富民兴鲁”五一劳动奖章。2010 年，上海世博会期间，为山东省人民政府设计制作了“泰岱旭日”和“富贵牡丹”看盘。

Chen Zeng—
Inheritor of Weifang Silver-inlaid Lacquerware

Chen Zeng, male, was born in 1945 in Weifang City, Shandong Province. He is an inheritor of Weifang silver-inlaid lacquerware.

During the Qing Dynasty, the copper jewelry craftsmen in Weixian tried to inlay metallic ornaments on copper ware by using the decorative techniques of fine metal workmanship of ancient utensils. Later, the coppersmiths experimented with inlaying metallic thread on small wooden ware. Later, after development, the Weifang silver-inlaid lacquerware is made of precious hardwood (mainly mahogany). It is precious, elegant and glittering.

Chen Zeng started to show his love in painting in his childhood. He was very fond of Weifang's traditional arts and crafts, especially the silver-inlaid lacquering skills. In 1960, Chen Zeng took part in the work, immediately acknowledged Guo Yuchun and Chen Kaixun, the fourth-generation inheritors of Weifang silver-inlaid lacquerware as his masters, and systematically learned woodworking, engraving, silver inlaying and lacquering techniques. With the teachers' careful training and his unremitting efforts, he mastered the whole process skillfully and accumulated rich experience. On the basis of predecessors, he inherited and developed, pioneered and innovated the craftsmanship, and achieved the perfect combination of engraving and silver inlaying.

In the aspect of engraving, Chen Zeng has combined traditional Chinese technique with Western flower patterns, and continuously make innovation to achieve the perfect combination of Chinese and Western products in style and craftsmanship; in the aspect of silver inlaying, he fully utilizes ancient flowers, birds and figures and various auspicious patterns, and draws patterns by means of line drawing, so that each product is novel but with traditional style. Unlike others, Mr. Chen integrates woodworking, engraving, silver inlaying and lacquering techniques. He is not only good at hands-on operation, but also have reached a new level of craftsmanship in design and creation of new products.

Chen Zeng not only keeps his innovative vigor and strives to improve his silver-inlaid lacquering skills, but also pays close attention to the innovative development of Weifang silver-inlaid lacquerware technique and the cultivation of inheritors. He has trained many inheritors. whose products have won many awards. Over the years, Mr. Chen has won many honors with his exquisite technique. In 1986, a smoking set designed and manufactured by Mr. Chen was awarded the first prize by Shandong Arts & Crafts Exhibition. In 1989, he created the landing screen "Spring Tide" for the Shandong Hall of the Great Hall of the People in Beijing. In 1995, Mr. Chen was awarded the May Day Labor Medal of Shandong Province. In 2010, during the Shanghai World Expo, he designed and manufactured "Mountain Tai Sunrise" and "Rich Peony" artworks for People's Government of Shandong Province.

柘砚制作技艺传承人——杨玉祯

杨玉祯，男，1937 年出生，山东泗水人，济宁市民间艺术家，现任泗水县鲁柘砚工艺研究所所长。

柘砚，又名“东鲁柘砚”“ 柘沟石砚”，因产于周朝鲁国属地柘沟而得名。从大汶口文化晚期遗址可以看出，当时柘沟的先民就烧制陶器。秦汉时期，制陶业生产延伸至文化用品领域，书写用的研磨器鲁柘砚也随着文化的繁荣应运而生。鲁柘砚是以过滤的优质原始黏土成坯雕饰、烧制而成，制作工艺复杂，全部手工完成。其质地细腻，温润如玉，就形设色，层次分明，具有质坚如玉、扶如童肌、声若金石等特点。

从西汉到 19 世纪末，柘沟就有家族制砚记载。杨玉祯师从柘沟老制砚艺人李庆元，学习鲁柘砚的制作技艺，后又成立鲁柘砚工艺研究所，专门开发研制柘砚。

柘砚制作工期长，工序复杂，从选料 、配料、澄泥、制坯、整形、雕刻、打磨、装匣、焙烧、出窑、修整、抛光，到装盒要经过近 20 道工序。杨玉祯在继承传统制砚技艺的同时，不断对鲁柘砚的澄泥、造型、雕刻、打磨、焙烧等各个环节进行大胆的探索和改革，现已研制成功上百种石砚。同时，他掌握了稀有色彩的特殊处理方法，将竹叶、松柏叶、花朵、粟粒等烧于墨堂和砚背上，使之出现逼真而又朦胧的图像，大大丰富了鲁柘砚的花色和品种。其质地、造型、色泽、实用方面，都优于同类产品。

鲁柘砚被指定参加山东（国际）文化产业博览会，后被授予“中华人民共和国第十一届运动会指定产品”称号。多年来，杨玉祯利用已经掌握的知识和经验，采取授课、示范、观摩交流、外出参观、“以师带徒” 等方式，亲自传授并培养澄泥砚制作工人，使这项传统制作技艺数十名得到较好的传承。

Yang Yuzhen— Inheritor of Zhe Inkstone Making Technique

Yang Yuzhen, male, was born in 1937 in Sishui County, Shandong Province. He is a folk artist in Jining City and currently the director of Luzhe Inkstone Technique Research Institute in Sishui County.

Zhe Yan, or Zhe Inkstone, also known as "Donglu Zhe Inkstone" and "Zhegou Inkstone" was named for its origin in Zhegou, the territory of the State of Lu in the Zhou Dynasty. From the site of the late Dawenkou Culture, we can see that the ancestors in Zhegou made pottery at that time. During the Qin and Han Dynasties, the production of ceramics extended to the field of cultural goods, and Luzhe inkstone came into being with the prosperity of culture. Luzhe inkstone is made of filtered high-quality clay, which is engraved and kilned into inkstone. Its manufacturing process is complicated and all done by hand. Its texture is delicate and moist as jade, and its shape and color are distinct. It is as solid as jade, feels like baby's skin, and sounds like metal and stone.

From the Western Han Dynasty to the end of the 19th century, there were records of family-made inkstone in Zhegou. Yang Yuzhen learned Zhe inkstone making technique from Li Qingyuan, a veteran inkstone craftsman in Zhegou. Later, he established the Luzhe Inkstone Technique Research Institute, which specializes in the development of Zhe inkstone.

The production period of Zhe inkstone is long and the process is complicated. It must go through nearly 20 procedures, from material selection, proportioning, filtering, shaping, reshaping, engraving, grinding, molding, kilning and polishing to packaging. While inheriting the traditional inkstone making technique, Mr. Yang has constantly carried out bold explorations and reforms in various procedures such as filtering, shaping, engraving, grinding, kilning and so on. Now hundreds of inkstones have been successfully developed. At the same time, he mastered the special methods of treating with rare colors, kilning bamboo leaves, pine and cypress leaves, flowers and millets on the front and back of inkstones, making it show realistic while hazy images, greatly enriching the colors and varieties of Luzhe inkstone. Its texture, shape, color and practicality are superior to those of the same kind.

Luzhe inkstone was appointed to participate in Shandong (International) Cultural Industry Expo, and was later awarded the title of "Designated Products of the 11th National Games of the People's Republic of China". Over the years, through such approaches as teaching, demonstration, exchage visit and apprenticeship, Yang Yuzhen has transferred his knowledge and experience to dozens of inkstone production workers, so that this traditional craftsmanship be better inherited.

聊城牛筋腰带制作技艺传承人——梁成贵

梁成贵，男，1959 年出生，山东聊城东昌府区人，现任聊城市御封工艺腰带有限公司经理。

牛筋腰带，又名“凉带”，是东昌府区独有的一种纯手工民间传统工艺品之一，始创于清初，成熟于乾隆年间。在明清两代，东昌府漕运发达。黄河以北，溯流而上，纤夫众多，束腰工具既要坚韧不断，又要耐水腐蚀，黄牛牛皮便是首选，牛筋腰带遂成最佳。经过数百年的演变和发展，经民间艺人的创造和传承，至清乾隆后成为结实耐用、古朴典雅、百姓喜爱的民间工艺品。

1975 年在本村师傅的指导下，梁成贵学习并掌握了牛筋腰带的编织技术。1980 年，他为聊城县工艺美术厂加工牛皮线，同时熟练掌握了腰带编织、修理、整形等全套技术。原始腰带料大花大间隙大，只能靠油漆来稳定它的形状，所以产品轮廓不清晰、没有柔软性。后经梁成贵改良的腰带不仅样式精细、结构紧凑，而且美观科学、轮廓清晰。为适应市场的需求，梁成贵摸索改进腰带花纹的编制工艺。经过和当地老师傅的潜心研究，花纹别致的“乾隆带”“一条龙”“五龙带”“古钱花”问世。之后他又改原始“勾式腰带”为“卡式腰带”，是腰带改进技术的一次革新。

牛筋腰带是选用优质牛皮为原料，手工切割，手工编织，经过多道独特的民间传统工艺编制而成。梁成贵制作的牛筋腰带坚固耐用，通风透凉，四季适宜，不仅式样美观大方，而且结构外紧内稀，耐拉力强，做工精细，形体整齐，具有清凉透气、束腰健身的效能。使用方便，男女皆宜，既有使用价值，又有较好的保健作用，深受大众欢迎，市场前景广阔。

2002 年，牛筋腰带被聊城市消费者协会确定为“向消费者推荐产品”；2003 年，被全国旅游商品博览会组委评为金奖产品；2006 年，被聊城市经贸委、聊城市旅游局评为第一届“水城集团杯”旅游商品大赛名优商品展销会工艺品类三等奖。

Liang Chenggui—Inheritor of Liaocheng Cattle-hide-made Belt Making Technique

Liang Chenggui, male, was born in 1959 in Dongchangfu District, Liaocheng City, Shandong Province, is currently the manager of Liaocheng Royal Craft Belt Co., Ltd.

Cattle-hide-made belt, also known as "cool belt", is one of the exclusive traditional handmade folk crafts in Dongchangfu District. It was originated in the early Qing Dynasty and matured during the reign of Emperor Qianlong. In the Ming and Qing Dynasties, the water transport of Dongchangfu was prosperous. To the north of the Yellow River, going upstream, there were many boat trackers. The belt for them should be both tough and water-resistant. Cattle hide was the first choice, and cattle-hide-made belt was the best product. After hundreds of years of evolution and development, through the creation and inheritance of folk artists, cattle-hide-made belt has become a solid, durable, simple, elegant and well received folk craft loved since the reign of Emperor Qianlong of the Qing Dynasty.

In 1975, under the guidance of artisans in the village, Liang Chenggui mastered the weaving technique of cattle-hide-made belt. In 1980, he worked for Liaocheng County Arts and Crafts Factory to process cattle hide thread, and at the same time, he mastered the complete set of techniques such as belt weaving, repairing and shaping. The original belt material has large gaps and can only be stabilized by paint, so the product contour is unclear and the texture is inflexible. The belt improved by Mr. Liang is not only exquisite in style and compact in structure, but also scientific in structure and clear in contour. In order to meet the needs of the market, Mr. Liang explored to improve the weaving technique of belt pattern. After careful study with local artisans, the Qianlong Belt, the One-Dragon Belt, the Five-Dragon Belt and Ancient Coin Belt with

unique patterns were produced. Later, he changed the original hook belt to buckle belt, which is an innovation of belt improvement technique.

Cattle-hide-made belt is made of high-quality cattle hide, hand-cut, and hand-woven, and is made through several unique traditional folk handicrafts. The cattle-hide-made belt made by Liang Chenggui is sturdy and durable, ventilated and cool, and suitable for all seasons. It is not only beautiful in appearance, but also compact in structure, strong in tension resistance, fine in workmanship, neat in shape, and it is cool for one's waist and good for one's health. It is easy to use and suitable for both male and female. It is well received by the public and has a broad market prospect.

In 2002, cattle-hide-made belt was recognized as "recommended products to consumers" by Liaocheng Consumers Association; in 2003, it was awarded the golden prize by the Organizing Committee of National Tourism Commodity Expo; in 2006, it was awarded the third prize of Arts & Crafts Category in the first "Shuicheng Group Cup" Famous and Excellent Tourism Commodities Fair by Liaocheng Economic and Trade Commission and Liaocheng Tourism Bureau.

聊城铁公鸡制作技艺传承人——魏炳田

魏炳田，男，1947年出生，山东聊城东昌府人。

“聊城铁公鸡”是中国语言大师老舍先生1935年夏赠给远香斋魏氏熏鸡的誉号。1935年夏，老舍先生在青岛与朋友聚会，品尝到魏氏熏鸡。由于其皮色黑里泛紫，活像京戏里铁面无私的黑老包，故老舍先生为其赐名“铁公鸡”。后经几代人改良传承，远销京、津、苏各地，销量大增，名声大振。

“魏氏熏鸡”由魏永泰在1810年独创，至今已有200余年的历史。魏炳田自1984年开始随父学习聊城铁公鸡制作技艺，是“魏氏熏鸡”第六代传人。从1994年至今，魏炳田一直生产经营魏氏熏鸡，期间由家庭式作坊发展为专业生产加工企业。随后他又把祖传的熏鸡制作技艺传授给了其兄弟和儿子，使这一技艺在家族得到很好的传承。

魏炳田制作的魏氏熏鸡以选料考究、调配合理、制作精细而著称。制作技艺独具特色，制作要经过15道精密工序。选用肥嫩良种活鸡，经卤煮，用锯末烟熏制而成。成品鸡皮缩裂，胸腿肉外露，色泽栗红，嚼有余香，脱水适宜，易于存放，便于携带，既可下酒，又可佐茶，是宴请宾客之美肴，馈赠亲朋之佳品。魏氏熏鸡风味独特，鲜香筋韧，广受大众喜爱，市场销量大增。在魏炳田的带动下，魏氏家族共开设3个门店，每个店年生产销售魏氏熏鸡10万余只，被列为“聊城名吃”之首。

1986年，魏炳田参加山东省首届鲁菜大赛获优秀奖，又获得2001年中国农业博览会“名牌产品”“鲁西名吃”“1998世界蓝天标志产品”等称号，1999年被确认为“中华老字号”。魏炳田将魏氏熏鸡的制作技艺不断发扬光大，为其传承和发展做出了重要贡献。

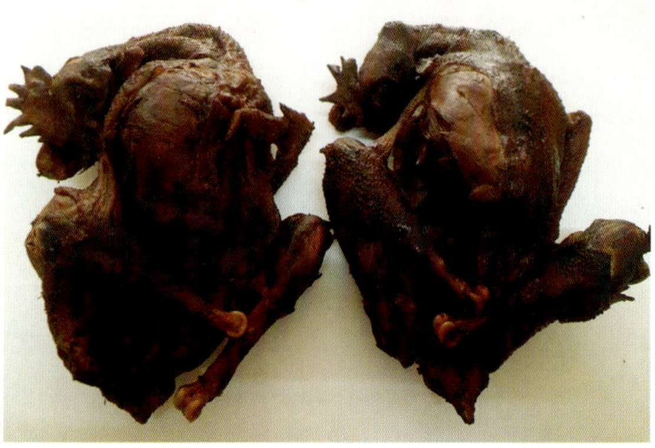

Wei Bingtian—Inheritor of Liaocheng Iron Rooster Making Technique

Wei Bingtian, male, was born in 1947 in Dongchangfu District Liaocheng City, Shandong Province.

The name "Liaocheng Iron Rooster" is given by Lao She, a Chinese language master, to Wei's smoked chicken in the summer of 1935. In the summer of 1935, Mr. Lao She gathered with friends in Qingdao and tasted Wei's smoked chicken. Because its skin is as black as iron, and it looks like a selfless black-faced Justice Bao in Beijing Opera, Mr. Lao She named it "Iron Rooster". After several generations of improvement and inheritance, it has been sold to Beijing, Tianjin and Jiangsu, with a large increase in sales and brought itself a great fame.

Wei's smoked chicken was originally created by Wei Yongtai in 1810 and has a history of more than 200 years. Since 1984, Wei Bingtian began to learn the skill of making Liaocheng iron rooster with his father. He is the sixth-generation inheritor of Wei's smoked chicken. From 1994 till now, Mr. Wei has been producing and managing Wei's smoked chicken, during which the family workshop developed into a professional production and processing enterprise. Then he imparted the ancestral technique of smoked chicken to his brothers and sons, so that this technique can be well inherited in the family.

Wei's Bingtian smoked chicken is famous for its exquisite material selection, excellent concoction and fine production. The production technique has its own characteristics, and it has to go through 15 precise procedures. Big and tender live chickens are selected, cooked in brine and smoked with sawdust. The finished chicken skin is cracked, the breast and leg meat is exposed, the color is chestnut red, the dehydration is appropriate. It is easy to store and carry, and goes well with wine tea. It is a great dish for banquet guests, a good gift to relatives and friends. The unique flavor of Wei's smoked chicken is widely loved by the public, and its market sales have increased greatly. Driven by Mr. Wei, the Wei family has opened three stores, each of which produces and sells more than 100,000 chickens annually, ranking as the first famous cuisine in Liaocheng.

In 1986, Wei Bingtian won the excellent award in the first Shandong Cuisine Competition in Shandong Province. His smoked chicken won the titles of "Famous Brand Product", "Famous Cuisine" in Western Shandong and "1998 World Blue Sky Mark Product" at the 2001 China Agricultural Expo. In 1999, Wei's smoked chicken was recognized as "Chinese Time-honored Brand". Mr. Wei has continuously promoted the production skills of Wei's smoked chicken and made important contributions to its inheritance and development.

胶南泊里红席编织技艺传承人——张学明

张学明，男，1972年出生，山东胶南泊里镇人。

泊里红席，俗称“秫秸席”，产于素有“红席之乡”美誉的胶南市泊里镇，是一种传统的纯手工艺制品。泊里红席是用高粱秆经去根、剔稍、捆坯子、破刮篾子、编隔子和挑席子等多道工序编织而成，因有红、白两种颜色，交叉编织出不同花纹的图案，故称“红席”。在泊里，几乎家家户户都有在炕上铺红席的习俗，红席成为婚嫁、逢年过节亲朋好友互相赠送的佳品。

张学明自幼跟随外公和父亲学习编织红席，利用业余时间专心研究改进红席编织技术，自己摸索出了一套独特的编席技巧。婚后，张学明与同样精通红席编织技艺的妻子相互切磋，技艺越发纯熟，不仅编席速度快，而且质量上乘、花色品种多样，是泊里镇年轻一辈编席匠人中的杰出代表。

张学明编出的泊里红席无毒无味，纯植物手工制作，编织紧密，纹理清晰，四角端正，编道整齐，具有光滑、柔软、美观、轻便、兜水不漏、结实耐用等特点。其席面色泽鲜艳、明亮，纹理平直、均匀；手感光滑，没有断秸、断筋、断边等现象，也无白梢、结疤等缺陷，深受民间喜爱。张学明还积极加入青岛泊里红席专业合作社，对红席的传统工艺不断改造，开发出了适合现代人使用的“双喜席”“福寿席”等10多个新品种，使泊里红席由过去的单纯农民“铺火炕”，逐渐成为城里人的时尚床上用品。

中华人民共和国成立初期，泊里红席曾作为本地土特产品，进京参加展出。张学明编织的红席曾获得“泊里镇第一届红席大赛”一等奖。到20世纪90年代在以张学明为首的编席匠人的带领下，泊里镇从事编红席的人数越来越多，泊里红席享誉胶东、东北等地。泊里红席编织带动了泊里镇的村民收入增长，并且辐射到周边乡镇，还出口日本、东南亚等国。

Zhang Xueming—Inheritor of Jiaonan Poli Red Mat Weaving Technique

Zhang Xueming, male, was born in 1972 in Poli Town, Jiaonan City, Shandong Province.

Poli red mat, commonly known as "Kaoliang stalk mat", is produced in Poli Town of Jiaonan City, known as "the hometown of red mat". It is a traditional handicraft. Poli red mat is made of kaoliang stalk by removing roots, getting rid of twigs, bundling base, cutting strips, weaving partitions and picking mat, etc. It is called "red mat" because it has two colors of red and white, which cross-weave different patterns. In Poli Town, almost every household has the custom of laying a red mat on the earthen bed. The red mat has become a good gift for relatives and friends in occasions such as marriage and festival.

Zhang Xueming learned to weave red mats with his grandfather and father in his childhood. He devoted his spare time to studying and improving the weaving technique of red mats, and developed a unique set of weaving skills by himself. After marriage, Mr. Zhang and his wife, who is equally proficient in red mat weaving, have consulted with each other and become more skilled. They not only weave mats quickly, but also endow their products with high quality and various designs. They are outstanding representatives of the young generation of mat weaving craftsmen in Poli Town.

The red mats woven by Zhang Xueming is non-toxic and odour-free. They are hand-made with natural plants. They have compact structure, clear texture, square corners and neat weaving lines. They are smooth, soft, beautiful, light, watertight and durable. The mat surface is bright in color, straight and even in texture. It is smooth in touch, with no stalk breakage, edge breakage, white shoots, scar or other defects, and is deeply loved by people. Mr. Zhang also actively joined the Qingdao Poli Red Mat Professional Cooperative, constantly reformed the traditional craftsmanship of the red mat weaving, and developed more than 10 new varieties suitable for modern people, such as "Double Happiness Mat" and "Happiness and Longevity Mat", which gradually made Poli red mat a fashionable bedding of urban people from the simple "bedding on earthen bed" by peasants in the past.

In the early days after the founding of the People's Republic of China, Poli red mat once participated in exhibition in Beijing as a native product. The red mat weaved by Zhang Xueming won the first prize of the first Red Mats Contest in Poli Town. In the 1990s, under the leadership of the mat weaving craftsmen headed by Mr. Zhang, more and more people were engaged in weaving red mats in Poli Town, and the product became well-known in Jiaodong and Northeast China. The red mat weaving has boosted the income of the villagers in Poli Town, and radiated to the surrounding towns, and has been exported to Japan, Southeast Asia and other countries.

长岛木帆船制造技艺传承人——刘延安

刘延安，男，1953年出生，山东长岛人，现任九龙船模厂厂长。

长岛木帆船制造技艺，源于长岛县渔业区的砣矶岛。清末民初，砣矶岛上的木帆船达300多只。木帆船按其造型、功能、运载的特点，可分为大风船、榷子和舢板。其中，大风船的载重最多，船体最大，续航能力最强。其建造工序大致分为铺志、比量口、上大绵梁三个阶段，共计20多道工序。在20世纪60年代末至70年代初，木帆船相继装机改造，木帆船修造业基本停止，与之相依存的木帆船制造技艺也处于濒危状态。

1967年，刘延安开始跟随外祖父学习帆船制造技术，是长岛木帆船制造技艺第四代传人。因其心灵手巧，勤学好问，外祖父便将宝贵的家传造船图纸传承予他。1971年，刘延安在砣矶镇渔轮厂参加工作，在参与制造木帆船、铁质渔轮的实践中，不断提高造船技能，成为一名技术精湛的木帆船制造工匠。1983年，刘延安参照岛上最后一只古帆船的制造尺寸和工艺，按照1:30的比例复制出古帆船模型，是长岛县为数不多的掌握仿古工艺的船模艺人。

刘延安制造长岛木帆船所用到的传统工艺技术难度大，技艺要求高，各构建的部位名称、功能作用均相当复杂。在制作中，大到桅舵、板材、梁柱，小到钉铆、滑轮、钩环，都一丝不苟；对木、铜、铁、铝，要因需施材，明处、暗处工艺一视同仁；从打磨、刨洗到组合，每一道工序，都要严丝合缝。在施工中，纯系手工操作，没有固定的图纸，只有心中的尺寸。凭借这一高超的技艺，刘延安设计复原制造出长岛县现在仅存的2只仿古大风船。

刘延安制作的船模《长岛仿古大帆船》在第五届中国民间工艺品博览会中获得金奖；船模《小号古帆船》等作品在旅游商品创新大赛中获得银奖、优秀奖等奖项；多项船模作品被不同部门收藏。刘延安将他的技术传授给后人，并教授来自本地、外地学习木帆船制造技术的艺人数十人，使长岛帆船的传统制造后继有人。

Liu Yan'an—Inheritor of Craftsmanship of Building Changdao Wooden Sailboat

Liu Yan'an, male, was born in 1953 in Changdao County, Yantai City, Shandong Province. He is the current the director of Jiulong Ship Model Factory.

The craftsmanship of building Changdao wooden sailboat originated in Tuoji Island in the fishery area in Changdao County. There were over 300 wooden sailboats on Tuoji Island in late Qing Dynasties. The wooden sailboats can be divided into Big-wind Boat, Quezi and Sampan. The Big-wind Boat is the vessel with greatest load, largest hull, and best endurance. The procedures mainly include over 20 steps in three stages—Puzhi (which means installing hull bottom), Biliangkou (which means putting a red cloth bag full of money at the center of the bottom when the construction meets 50% progress), Shangdamianliang (which means building the main support of the hull, marking the completion of the hull). In late 1960s and early 1970s, the wooden sailboats were successively renovated, and the wooden sailboat manufacture industry was almost shut down. Therefore, the craftsmanship of wooden sailboat derived from it is in danger.

In 1967, Liu Yan'an, the 4th-generation inheritor started to learn the craftsmanship of building wooden sailboat. Due to his ingenuity and diligence, his maternal grandfather has bestowed the precious shipbuilding blueprint handed down from ancestors upon him. In 1971, Mr. Liu got a job in a spinning reel factory in Tuoji town, and became a skilled craftsman by improving his skill of shipbuilding in his practice of building wooden sailboats and manufacturing spinning reels. In 1983, Mr. Liu duplicated a model of ancient sailboat in proportion of 1:30 compared with the size and craftsmanship of the last ancient sailboat on the Island. He is one of the few sailboat model craftsmen who master the skill of imitating the ancient sailboats.

The traditional craftsmanship of building Changdao wooden sailboat of Liu Yan'an is pretty complicated, and it requires high demands for skills. Besides, the components' names and their functions are very complex. During manufacturing, everything should be made meticulously, from mast, rudder, sheet material, and beam column to rivet, pulley, and looped link; the materials, such as wood, copper, iron, and aluminum, should be used based on different demands, and the craft of both the visible and invisible parts should be same; every procedure, from polishing and milling to combination, should be fastidious. All operations during construction are manual. There is no stereotypical blueprint, for the real blueprint exists inside the brain. By virtue of the superb skill, Mr. Liu designed and built the only existing two archaized Big-wind Boats.

The model Changdao archaized big sailboat made by Liu Yan'an won the golden award in the 5th Expo of Chinese Folk Craftsmanship. The model Small-Sized Ancient Sailboat won silver award and excellence award in Tourism Commodity Innovation Competition. Besides, there were also many models collected by various departments. Mr. Liu taught his craftsmanship to his later generations, including tens of craftsmen who are from local area and other places aiming to learn the craftsmanship of wooden sailboats, preparing qualified inheritors of the craftsmanship of building the traditional Changdao wooden sailboat.

济南油旋制作技艺传承人——卢利华

卢利华，女，1967 年出生，山东济南市市中区人，中式面点高级技师。

油旋最早出现于清代，距今已有 100 多年的历史。相传，油旋是清朝的徐氏三兄弟去南方闯荡时在南京学来的，油旋在南方的口味是甜的，徐氏兄弟来济南后依据北方人的饮食特点，将油旋的口味改成咸香味，一直传承至今。清道光年间，济南城里的凤集楼就有油旋经营。光绪二十年（1894 年）开业的文升园饭庄制作的油旋葱香浓郁，层次分明，外酥脆，内松软，颇受欢迎。1956 年后，聚丰德饭店制作的油旋因生产历史最长、最受泉城人的喜爱，成为济南名吃。

自 1982 年参加工作起，卢利华就师从原聚丰德饭店济南名吃油旋第二代传人苏将林学习济南油旋的制作技艺，成为聚丰德饭店的一名面点师，后又独自成立济南弘春美斋油旋专卖店。卢利华创立的济南弘春美斋真正实现了济南名吃油旋由原来的饭店生产间生产到现在的与消费者零距离展示性生产的转变。卢利华也从最初的面点学徒成长为一名中式面点高级技师。

卢利华制作的油旋是一种传统的手工艺面制品，生产工艺烦琐。具体步骤是将面粉加适量水、少许精盐，醒两小时后，下剂，擀皮；将擀好的皮抹猪大油、精盐、撒葱米，卷好（卷 60 层）制成生坯；将生坯放吊炉里烤至定型，取出；放在炉上层淋花生油烙制 10 分钟至金黄色。出炉后色泽金黄，外酥里嫩，香味浓郁，形如漩涡，故名油旋。

卢利华一直致力于济南传统名优面点油旋的制作、宣传与推广，技艺成熟以来已收徒三人，对济南油旋这一传统名吃的传承发挥了较大的促进作用。产品曾获得济南名优面点、济南名优（风味）小吃等荣誉。2011 年 5 月，获得中国烹饪协会颁发的“中华名小吃”称号。

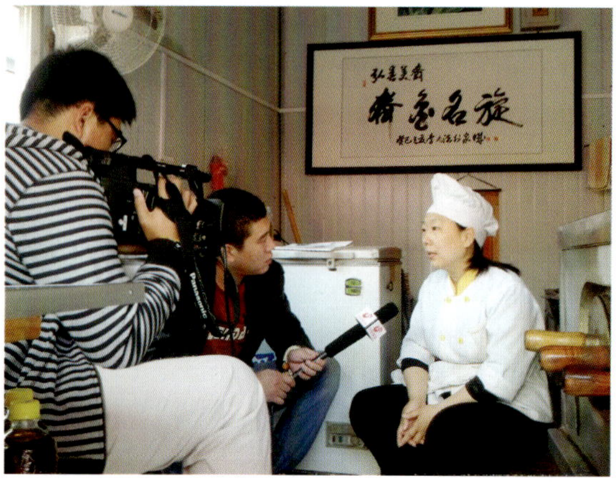

Lu Lihua— Inheritor of Craftsmanship of Making Jinan Oil Spin

Lu Lihua, female, was born in 1967 in the Shizhong District, Jinan City, Shandong Province. She is a senior technician of Chinese Dim Sum.

Oil spin ("youxuan" in Mandarin) first appeared in late Qing Dynasty in Jinan, having a history of over 100 years. It is said that oil spin was developed by three brothers from Xu family who learned it in Nanjing, a southern Chinese city. The flavor of oil spin in southern China is sugary, while the three brothers changed it to salty taste based on the diet characteristics of northern Chinese people. Therefore, the northern flavor is passed down from one generation to another. During the reign of Emperor Daoguang of the Qing Dynasty, people could buy oil spins in Fengji Building in Jinan. In the 20th year of Emperor Guangxu of the Qing Dynasty (i.e. 1894), the oil spins made by Wenshengyuan restaurant were fragrant with the flavor of scallions, well arranged, crispy on the outside and soft on the inside, so it became prevailing. After 1956, the oil spins made by Jufengde Restaurant, which had the longest history and were liked by people in Jinan, became Jinan's famous Cuisine.

Since she began to work in 1982, Lu Lihua has been learning the craftsmanship from Su Jianglin, the 2nd-generation inheritor of Jufengde Restaurant oil spin, thus becoming a pastry cook. Later on, Ms. Lu established Jinan Hongchunmeizhai Oil Spin Exclusive Shop, realizing the transformation from oil spin production inside restaurant kitchen to oil spin production displayed in front of consumers. Mr. Lu also changed her own identity from a pastry student to a senior technician of Chinese Dim Sum.

The oil spin made by Lu Lihua is a kind of traditional handmade flour product whose procedures are very complicated. The specific procedures include, firstly, pouring moderate water and some refined salt into flour, fermenting the flour for two hours, making jizi (dragging small pieces from the long flour stripe), and rolling jizi; secondly, wiping lard, refined salt, chopped scallions onto the mianpi (made by flattening jizi), and making raw pi by rolling mianpi (about 60 layers); thirdly, putting the raw pi into the oven to toast it until its shape is set, and then taking it out; and finally, baking it after pouring peanut oil on it until it turns golden. After it is taken out from the oven, it turns golden yellow, becomes crispy on the outside and soft on the inside, and emits fragrance. Its shape is like a vortex ("xuanwo" in Mandarin), hence its name "youxuan".

Lu Lihua has been devoting herself to the making, publicizing, and promotion of oil spins. After she becomes more and more skilled, she has taken three students, making great contributions to the inheritance of the traditional snack. The snack has won awards such as Jinan Famous & Fine Pastry, Jinan Famous & Fine Snack, etc. On May in 2011, the snack was awarded "Chinese Famous Snack" by China Cuisine Association.

傳承人

传统医药

Traditional Medicine

董家骨科正骨疗法传承人——董胜军

董胜军，男，1967年出生，山东安丘人，现任安丘市董家骨科研究所所长。

董家正骨疗法起源于山东省安丘市贾戈镇董家王封村，祖上几代均是“擅正骨”“通药理”之人。自清道光十二年（1832年）起，经董氏数代人的探索、研究、实践，董家骨科正骨疗法由单纯地治疗断胫折臂发展成为一门较完整的综合正骨科，并创“天德堂”正式行医。董家正骨经历了近200年的正骨历程，在民间有“接骨神仙”的美誉。

董胜军是董家骨科正骨疗法的第五代传人，他在继承四代董家骨科前辈正骨疗法的基础上，创办“董家骨科诊所”，将这一祖传正骨手法发扬光大。

董胜军在继承传统正骨八法的基础上，将正骨手法发展并完善为三大类手法，即诊断手法、复位手法和活筋手法。在医治方法上，董胜军发明了小夹板固定、粘贴固定、绑扎固定、器具固定、积淀固定、皮肤牵引固定等骨伤治疗绝招。在用药配方上，董胜军运用祖传秘方对骨病患者施以外敷、内服中药的辅助治疗，其研发的“鱼鳔接骨胶囊”“董氏接骨散”“灵术活血胶囊”等药物具有舒筋通络、活血化瘀、消肿止痛、祛风除湿、壮骨补肾等特效。董胜军经常深入农村，特别是偏远的山区，为骨伤病人诊治，以低廉的价格，热情的服务赢得了人民群众的赞誉。

“董家骨科”被评为首批“潍坊老字号”，获得了良好的声誉。为了将董家骨科的正骨手法传承下去，董胜军决定将这一家传技艺对外公开，服务百姓，惠及大众。鉴于董氏正骨的显著疗效和良好医德，有关卫生主管部门分别为董家骨科颁发了《医疗机构执业许可证》《医疗机构制剂许可证》，董胜军为中医正骨的传承做出了重要贡献。

Dong Shengjun—Inheritor of Dong's Orthopedics

Dong Shengjun, male, was born in 1967 in Anqiu County, Weifang City, Shandong Province. He is the current director of Anqiu Institute of Dong's Orthopedics.

Dong's orthopedics stems from Wangfeng Village, Jiage Town, Anqiu County, Shandong Province. Several ancestors of Dong's were all masters skilled in orthopedics and pharmacology. Since the 12th year of the reign of Emperor Daoguang of the Qing Dynasty (1832), Dong's orthopedics has been converted from purely curing broken bones to a complete comprehensive subject after exploration, research and practices by generations in Dong Family. In addition, Tian De Tang was also established by Dong's descendant. After developing for over 200 years, Dong's orthopedics of enjoy a good reputation among people, and Dong's descendants have been honored as "Gods of Bone-setting".

Dong Shengjun is the 5th-generation inheritor of Dong's orthopedics. On the basis of inheriting Dong's orthopedics therapy, Mr. Dong established Dong's Orthopedics Clinic, popularizing the orthopedics therapy handed down from his ancestors.

On the basis of inheriting the eight methods of traditional orthopedics, Dong Shengjun has developed it into three new kinds of methods including Diagnosis Method, Resetting method and Sinew-soothing Method. Besides, Mr. Dong also invented some treatment skills with respect to medical treatment including small splint fixation, pasting fixation, binding fixation, apparatus fixation, sediment fixation, skin traction fixation etc. And in respect of the ingredients of the medicine, Mr. Dong use medicines based on the prescription handed down from his ancestors, and prescrikes both orally taken medicines and externally applied one's. Medicines such as "Swim Bladder Bone-Setting Capsule" "Dong's Bone-Setting Powder", and "Blood Invigorating Capsule" etc. have the functions like stimulating blood circulation and relaxing muscles and joints, dissipating blood stasis, easing swelling and relieving pain, dispelling rheumatism, strengthening bones and kidney, etc. Mr. Dong visits villages very frequently, especially those in remote mountainous regions, to cure the patients who have been suffering from bone fracture at a low price. His service with enthusiasm earns him praise and commendation.

Dong's Orthopedics was awarded one of the first "Weifang Time-honored Brands" and has won a good fame. To further inherit Dong's orthopedics, Dong Shengjun decided to teach the traditional skills to the public, serving the people and benefiting the public. Given the curative property and great medical ethics, Dong's orthopedics has been granted with Practice License of Medical Institution and Pharmaceutical Preparation License for Medical Institutions. Mr. Dong has made great contributions to the inheriting of traditional Chinese orthopedics.

安驾庄梁氏正骨疗法传承人——梁盛兴

梁盛兴，男，1950 年出生，山东肥城人，现任肥城市安驾庄梁氏正骨医院院长。

安驾庄梁氏正骨源于肥城市南部的安驾庄村，由梁增生始创于清雍正末年，距今已有 200 多年的历史，是我国为数不多的祖传正骨派系之一。清末，梁氏正骨在第四代传人梁桂荣时期，得到了很大发展。梁桂荣继承先人经验，经多年临床实践，进一步完善了梁氏膏药的配方及熬制方法，后又博取众家之长，创出托举、折顶、屈曲、牵抖等 14 种治疗手法，主治四肢闭合性和简单开放性骨折与脱臼。

梁盛兴出生于梁氏正骨世家，初中毕业后，到山东省立医院跟随祖父梁荫铣先生（第五代传承人）学习祖传正骨手法。之后又受父亲梁洪斌言传身教十余年，秉承祖辈医德，领悟正骨要术。

梁盛兴继承的安驾庄梁氏正骨疗法，采用独特医疗手法，讲究“法”从手起，力度轻重适宜，体现稳、准、狠、快；在医疗配方上，梁氏膏药，药材选配严谨，熬制工序独特；用药时，注重固护和恢复人体正气，辨证施治，处方严谨，实施三期服（敷）药、内外兼治，内服汤剂，外敷膏药，加速骨骼创面愈合，后期导之以功能锻炼，附加中药汤洗。梁盛兴独创的杉树皮小夹板，利于膏药药性渗透，加速骨折部位的愈合，康复后可负重劳动。安驾庄梁氏正骨所用器具简单，可就地取材，自己制作，因此成本低，费用少，康复较快，大大减轻了骨伤患者的经济负担。

梁盛兴医术高明，医德高尚，多年来治愈骨伤患者无数，在当地有口皆碑，为梁氏正骨疗法的传承做出了重要贡献。

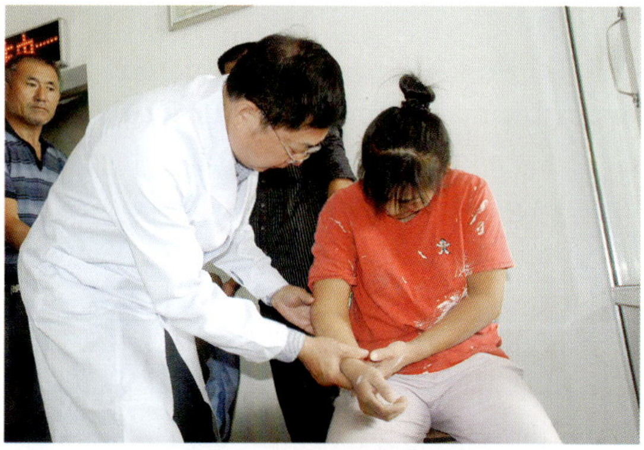

传统医药

Liang Shengxing—Inheritor of Liang's Bone-setting Therapy in Anjiazhuang Town

Liang Shengxing, male, was born in 1950 in Feicheng City, Shandong Province. He is now the head of Liang Bone-setting Hospital in Anjiazhuang Town, Feicheng City.

Liang bone-setting therapy originated from Anjiazhuang village in the south of Feicheng City. It was started by Liang Zengsheng in the late period of the reign of Yongzheng Emperor in the Qing Dynasty and has a history of more than 200 years. It is one of the few ancestral bone-setting factions in China. During the period of the fourth-generation inheritor Liang Guirong in the late Qing Dynasty, Liang's bone-setting therapy made a huge progress. Liang Guirong inherited the experience of his ancestors, and after years of clinical practice, he further improved the formula and decoction method of Liang's plaster. Later, he gained the advantages of others and created 14 treatment methods such as lifting, folding, buckling and shaking, which were mainly used to treat closed and open fractures and dislocations of limbs.

Liang Shengxing was born in a family of bone-setting doctors. After graduating from junior high school, he went to Shandong Provincial Hospital to learn the technique of bone-setting from his grandfather, Liang Yinxian (the fifth-generation inheritor). Later, he followed the teaching of his father Liang Hongbin for more than ten years, and finally inherited the ancestral medical ethics and understood the knacks of bone-setting.

Liang's bone-setting therapy inherited by Liang Shengxing adopts unique medical techniques and pays attention to the "technique" of hands with appropriate intensity, reflecting stability, accuracy, firmness and rapidity. In the medical formula, the herbal material selection of Liang's plaster is strict and the boiling process is unique. When using the medicine, Mr. Liang focuses on caring and recovering the healthy Qi inside the body. Mr. Liang makes thorough diagnosis and treatment based on an overall analysis of the illness and the patient's condition. The patient is treated by three phases by taking decoction orally and applying plaster externally to accelerate the healing of bone wound. At a later stage, the patient is encouraged to take exercises and uses Chinese medicine decoction to wash the wounded part. Mr. Liang's original fir bark splint is beneficial to the penetration of the ointment and accelerates the healing of the fracture site. The patient can work with heavy load after recovery. Mr. Liang's bone-setting apparatus is simple and can be made by oneself with local materials. With low cost and quick recovery, the method greatly reduces the economic burden of patients with bone injuries.

Liang Shengxing is excellent in medical skills and noble in medical ethics. Over the years, he has cured countless patients with bone injuries, and is well recognized locally. He has made important contributions to the inheritance of Liang's bone-setting therapy.

傳承人

民俗
Folk Customs

桃源花供传承人——徐保忠

徐保忠，男，1955 年出生，山东曹县桃源镇人。

桃源花供是曹县桃源集居民把面塑、蔬菜制作成花供祭祀火神的一种民俗活动。桃源花供的供品最初是用白面制作而成，后来又改为用当地盛产的白萝卜为原料，供品花样增多，所以称为“花供”，火神会也就成为花供会。桃源花供活动主要包括搭神棚、搭彩棚、进香、做花供、朝台进供等具体内容。其中，最重要的是做花供和朝台进供。做花供从正月初六下午开始准备各种材料、器具，选好地方，然后聚集工匠一起制作；朝台进供从正月初七上午 9 点开始，每隔半个钟头进供一次。数万人随花供队伍行进至搭建的彩棚处，边走边看摆放好的花供，场面十分热闹。

徐保忠从 21 岁起，就随街邻学习花供的制作技艺，是桃源花供的第三代传人。在做花供的过程中，徐保忠根据“口传心授”的经验，对各种花供材料有了更深刻的了解，使花供的制作具有鲜明的技艺特征。徐保忠在制作花供过程中，显示出独特的制作技巧，工艺性强。在造型、绘色等技艺中显现出独具特色的地方民俗色彩。其丰富的题材，色彩搭配的讲究，都是对生活的艺术化提炼，展现了独具匠心的审美思维和高超的技艺。

桃源花供是独特的祭祀火神形式，显示了桃源集与众不同的文化发展背景及历史渊源。通过举办花供这一传统民俗活动，加强了不同宗族、姓氏之间的相互往来，消除了彼此间的矛盾与隔阂，起到了增强民族凝聚力和向心力的重要作用。由于徐保忠对桃源花供这一传统民间习俗做了大量的抢救和宣传工作，被授予“曹县民间手工技艺大师”荣誉称号。

随着人们文化生活的日益丰富，娱乐活动越来越广泛，年轻人普遍对桃源花供传统习俗缺乏足够的欣赏力。愿意学习、传承花供技艺的人少之又少，桃源花供这一民俗活动的生存空间越来越小，逐步走向衰微，只有加强保护和扶持，才是对桃源花供民俗文化的最好传承。

Xu Baozhong—
Inheritor of Taoyuan Variety Offering

Xu Baozhong, male, was born in 1955 in Taoyuanji Town, Cao County, Shandong Province.

Taoyuan variety offering is a folk activity in Taoyuanji Town, Cao County, where residents make dough figurines and vegetables into offerings to the God of Fire. Taoyuan variety offerings were originally made of white flour and later of locally abundant white radish. The variety of offerings increased, so it was called "Variety Offering" and the God of Fire Ceremony became Taoyuan Variety Offering Ceremony. The activities of Taoyuan variety offering mainly include setting up a colorful shed for the god, offering incense, making various offerings, and worshiping the god. Among them, making various offering and worshiping the god are the two most important parts. On the afternoon of the sixth day of the first lunar month, people will prepare various materials and utensils, choose a place, and gather artisans to make offerings together. The worship service starts at 9 am on the seventh day of the first lunar month and is held every half hour. Tens of thousands of people followed the variety offering procession to the colorful shed and appreciated the variety offerings as they walked. It was a lively scene.

From the age of 21, Xu Baozhong followed his neighbors to learn making offerings. Now, he is the third-generation inheritor of Taoyuan Variety Offering. During the learning process, Mr. Xu was inspired by his neighbors' experience. Thus, Mr. Xu had a deeper understanding of all kinds of offering materials which featured his work with distinct personal characteristics. Mr. Xu has unique production skills, and shows exquisite craftsmanship. The modeliny, painting and other techniques characterize his work with a unique local folk color. The rich themes and attention to color matching of his work are reflections of Mr. Xu's artistic way of life, showing his unique aesthetic thinking and superb skills as well.

Taoyuan variety offering is a unique form of offering sacrifices to the God of Fire, which shows the distinctive cultural background and historical origin of Taoyuanji town. Through the traditional folk activity of Taoyuan variety offering, it strengthens the interaction between different clans and surnames, eliminates the contradiction and estrangement between them, and plays an important role in enhancing national cohesion and centripetal force. Xu Baozhong was awarded the honorary title of "Master of Folk Handicraft in Cao County" for his rescue and promotion of the traditional folk custom.

However, with the increasingly rich cultural life and more extensive recreational activities, young people generally lack sufficient appreciation of the traditional folk custom of Taoyuan variety offering. Few people nowadays are willing to learn and inherit the art of Taoyuan variety offering, so the living space of the folk activity becomes smaller and is gradually declining. Only by strengthening protection and support can people best inherit the Taoyuan variety offering folk culture.

祭孔大典传承人——李文广

李文广，男，1966年出生，山东曲阜人，“济宁市优秀演员”，现任曲阜市山东梆子剧团团长。

祭孔大典是山东曲阜专门祭祀孔子的大型庙堂乐舞活动，亦称“丁祭乐舞”或“大成乐舞”，是集乐、歌、舞、礼为一体的综合性艺术表演形式，最早可追溯到公元前478年。祭孔大典紧紧围绕“礼”而进行，用音乐舞蹈等艺术形式集中表现儒家思想文化，具有较强艺术感染力和精神凝聚力，并借助中国曲阜国际孔子文化节上的表演成为世界性文化遗产。

李文广于1981年就职于曲阜市剧团暨曲阜市古乐舞；1986年，参与祭孔大典的研究、挖掘、整理、完善。自恢复祭孔仪式以来，他从事有关祭孔的礼乐活动已经整整33年。不仅参与了“孔子故里游”活动开幕式的演出，而且还参加了历届国际孔子文化节的祭孔大典演出。此外，他还多次参加接待中外领导人的专场演出，并应邀到全国各地演出。

李文广具有较丰富的古代祭仪学识和演出实践经验，在演出中相继担任过八佾舞舞生、礼生、司礼官等角色，为祭孔大典的不断完善奠定了良好的基础。李文广参与的音乐、舞蹈表演形象地阐释孔子学说中“礼”的涵义，表达“仁者爱人”“以礼立人”的思想，突出展现“千古礼乐归东鲁，万古衣冠拜素王”的盛况。另外，作为专家学者团的一员，他对现行祭孔大典的主要程序、重要礼制、祭品祭器、乐舞祝文等进行了科学严谨的考据和论证，既致力参照古制程序、重现传统魅力，又努力提升庆典效果、凸显文化品味。

多年来，李文广一直专注于祭孔大典研习，保证了一年一度的中国曲阜国际孔子文化节的《祭孔大典》表演。李文广参与的歌舞表演多次获得一等奖并被评为优秀演员和先进个人。他在山东省民间艺术展演中祭孔大典获“绿牡丹奖”。为了祭孔大典更好的推广，他自己组织了全国的培训班，让各地的儒学爱好者前来学习，积极培养下一批的祭孔大典传承人。

Li Wenguang—
Inheritor of Confucius Memorial Ceremony

Li Wenguang, male, was born in 1966 in Qufu City, Shandong Province. He is an Outstanding Actor of Jining City. He is now the head of Shandong Clapper Opera Troupe in Qufu city.

Confucius memorial ceremony is a large-scale temple music and dance activity in memory of Confucius in Qufu City, Shandong Province, which is also called "Dingji music and dance" or "Dacheng music and dance". It is a comprehensive form of artistic performance integrating music, song, dance and ritual, which can be traced back to 478 BC at the earliest. The ceremony focuses on "rites", and shows the Confucian culture through music, dance and other art forms. It has a strong artistic appeal and spiritual cohesion, and becomes a world cultural heritage by virtue of the performance at the International Confucius Culture Festival in Qufu.

Li Wenguang worked in Qufu Opera Troupe in 1981. In 1986, he participated in the research, excavation, collation and improvement of the ceremony. Since resuming the ceremony, he has been engaged in the ritual and music activities for 33 years. He not only participated in the performance of the opening ceremony of "Confucius' Hometown Tour", but also was a member of the performance at the International Confucius Culture Festival held in the past years. In addition, he has been a performer in many special performances for Chinese and foreign leaders and has been invited to perform all over the country.

Li Wenguang has rich knowledge of ancient ritual and performance practice experience and has served as Eight Yiwu dancer (Eight Yiwu is the highest-level sacrificial dance in ancient China), ritual host, officiating host and other roles in the performance, which have laid a good foundation for the continuous improvement of the ceremony. The music and dance performances in which Mr. Li participated vividly explained the meaning of "the rules of proper conduct" in Confucian theory and expressed the thought of "The benevolent loves others" and "cultivate a person by propriety", which highlights the grand occasion of "The ancient rites and music belong to Donglu (where Confucius lived), and as long as human history and culture exist, the power and influence of Confucius will always exist". In addition, as a member of panel of experts, he has carried out scientific and rigorous textual research and demonstration on the main procedures, important ritual systems, sacrificial vessels, music, dance and ritual oration as well as other aspects of the current Confucius memorial ceremony. He devoted himself to reproducing the traditional charm by referring to the ancient procedures, and also to improving the effect of the ceremony and highlighting the cultural taste.

For many years, Li Wenguang has been focusing on studying the Confucius memorial ceremony, guaranteeing its annual performance at the International Confucius Culture Festival in Qufu China. Mr. Li has participated in many singing and dancing performances, which have brought him the first prize and the titles of excellent actor and advanced individual for many times. His performance at the Confucius memorial ceremony won the "Green Peony Award" in the folk art performance in Shandong Province. In order to better promote the Confucius memorial ceremony, Mr. Li organized a national training class for Confucianism enthusiasts from all over the country and engaged himself actively in cultivation of the next batch of inheritors of the Confucius memorial ceremony.

附录一

关于公布第三批省级非物质文化遗产项目代表性传承人的通知

各市文广新局、省直文化系统有关单位：

为贯彻《中华人民共和国非物质文化遗产法》、国务院办公厅《关于加强我国非物质文化遗产保护工作的意见》和鲁政办发〔2005〕94号的精神和有关规定，省文化厅组织开展了第三批省级非物质文化遗产项目代表性传承人的申报和评审工作。经各地申报、专家评审委员会评审、社会公示等程序，最后确定了马镇华等62人为山东省第三批省级非物质文化遗产项目代表性传承人，现予以公布。

省级非物质文化遗产项目代表性传承人是非物质文化遗产的重要承载者和传递者，是非物质文化遗产活态传承的代表性人物。各市、各有关部门要认真贯彻“保护为主、抢救第一、合理利用、传承发展”的工作方针，积极落实各项保护措施，鼓励非物质文化遗产代表性传承人开展传习活动，为他们创造良好的传习环境，推动非物质文化遗产传承和发扬，为弘扬中华文化，建设中华民族共有精神家园，推动社会主义文化大发展大繁荣，构建社会主义和谐社会，做出新的贡献。

特此通知。

山东省文化厅

2011年1月21日

附录二

山东省第三批省级非物质文化遗产项目代表性传承人名单

（共62人）

传统舞蹈10人

序号	项目编码	项目名称	申报地区或单位	代表性传承人		
				姓名	性别	年龄
1	Ⅲ-26	小章竹马	昌邑市	马镇华	男	72
2	Ⅲ-23	地秧歌	高密市	王兆章	男	73
3	Ⅲ-36	闹海	寿光市	黄冠群	女	51
4	Ⅲ-32	三皇舞	鄄城县	魏凤莲	女	64
5	4-7	陈官短穗花鼓	广饶县	张兰青	女	40
6	4-17	阴阳板	邹城市	王长军	男	46
7	Ⅲ-29	火虎	邹城市	周长来	男	56
8	Ⅲ-34	蹉地舞	莱芜市莱城区	黄象浩	男	56
9	Ⅲ-35	猴呱哒鞭	苍山县	张学法	男	82
10	Ⅲ-33	柳林降狮舞	冠县	杨乃让	男	48

传统戏剧10人

序号	项目编码	项目名称	申报地区或单位	代表性传承人		
				姓名	性别	年龄
11	Ⅳ-1	柳子戏（宋家班）	定陶县	刘进武	男	82
12	Ⅳ-1	柳子戏（宋家班）	定陶县	赵新文	男	64
13	Ⅳ-8	吕剧	滨州市	王永昌	男	75
14	5-8	吕剧	山东省文化厅	胡静华	女	47
15	5-8	吕剧	山东省文化厅	马常委	男	52

16	5-3	茂腔	胶州市	张梅香	女	61
17	5-18	山亭皮影戏	枣庄市山亭区	陈守科	男	51
18	5-7	京剧	山东省文化厅	白云明	男	66
19	5-7	京剧	山东省文化厅	王玉瑾	男	74
20	5-7	京剧	山东省文化厅	薛亚萍	女	65

曲艺 7 人

序号	项目编码	项目名称	申报地区或单位	代表性传承人		
				姓名	性别	年龄
21	V-13	东路大鼓	安丘市	丁淑红	女	45
22	V-13	东路大鼓	滨州市滨城区	周金山	男	71
23	6-9	端鼓腔	微山县	杨成兴	男	33
24	6-2	山东琴书	山东省文化厅	朱丽华	女	66
25	V-6	山东落子	金乡县	张青敏	男	50
26	6-3	山东快书	山东省文化厅	高景佐	男	78
27	V-11	评词	济南市	刘延广	男	72

传统体育、游艺与杂技 10 人

序号	项目编码	项目名称	申报地区或单位	代表性传承人		
				姓名	性别	年龄
28	Ⅵ-13	孙膑拳	安丘市	刘海港	男	40
29	Ⅵ-14	大洪拳	郓城县	樊庆斌	男	53
30	Ⅵ-16	佛汉拳	东明县	李义军	男	56
31	Ⅵ-9	梅花拳	梁山县	冯建武	男	43
32	Ⅵ-11	子午门	梁山县	宋义祥	男	41
33	7-1	聊城杂技	聊城市	王　峰	男	44
34	Ⅵ-21	临清肘锤（捶）	临清市	申孝生	男	66
35	4-13	螳螂拳	莱阳市	于永波	男	45
36	Ⅵ-12	徐家拳	新泰市	徐勤启	男	47
37	Ⅵ-19	济南形意拳	济南市	杨遵利	男	49

传统美术 8 人						
序号	项目编码	项目名称	申报地区或单位	代表性传承人		
				姓名	性别	年龄
38	Ⅶ-37	高密半印半画年画	高密市	别世杰	男	66
39	Ⅶ-34	茌平剪纸	茌平县	尹秀凤	女	61
40	2-3	宗家庄木版年画	平度市	宗成云	男	67
41	Ⅶ-33	威海剪纸	威海市	王言昌	男	70
42	Ⅶ-35	黄县窗染花	龙口市	王松生	男	67
43	2-25	滕县松枝鸟	滕州市	王德金	男	77
44	Ⅶ-38	鲁绣	济南市	徐秀玲	女	50
45	2-19	烟台剪纸	烟台市	王秀娥	女	62

传统技艺 14 人						
序号	项目编码	项目名称	申报地区或单位	代表性传承人		
				姓名	性别	年龄
46	Ⅶ-40	桑皮纸制作技艺	临朐县	魏先明	男	64
47	Ⅷ-24	青州府花边大套	青州市	卜范增	男	56
48	Ⅷ-23	曹县戏文纸扎	曹县	张于周	男	50
49	Ⅷ-3	蓝印花布印染技艺	滨州市	耿延祯	男	64
50	Ⅶ-3	蓝印花布印染技艺	嘉祥县	杜宗环	男	68
51	Ⅷ-2	彩印花布印染技艺	嘉祥县	李景春	男	56
52	8-12	潍坊嵌银漆器	潍坊市	陈　增	男	66
53	8-13	柘砚制作技艺	泗水县	杨玉祯	男	74
54	Ⅷ-35	聊城牛筋腰带制作技艺	聊城市东昌府区	梁成贵	男	52
55	Ⅷ-59	聊城铁公鸡制作技艺	聊城市东昌府区	魏炳田	男	64
56	Ⅷ-42	胶南泊里红席编织技艺	胶南市	张学明	男	44
57	Ⅷ-29	长岛木帆船制造技艺	长岛县	刘延安	男	58
58	Ⅷ-60	济南油旋制作技艺	济南市	卢利华	女	44

传统医药2人						
序号	项目编码	项目名称	申报地区或单位	代表性传承人		
				姓名	性别	年龄
59	Ⅸ-7	董家骨科正骨疗法	安丘市	董胜军	男	44
60	Ⅸ-6	安驾庄梁氏正骨疗法	肥城市	梁盛兴	男	61
民俗2人						
序号	项目编码	项目名称	申报地区或单位	代表性传承人		
				姓名	性别	年龄
61	X-16	桃源花供	曹县	徐保忠	男	64
62	1-14	祭孔大典	曲阜市	李文广	男	45

后记 EPILOGUE

《山东省省级非物质文化遗产项目代表性传承人》是山东省完整系统地介绍省级非遗项目代表性传承人的典籍，也是宣传山东省非物质文化遗产的重要工具书。本书记录着山东省省级非遗项目代表性传承人的基本情况、技艺特征、授徒传承等方面的内容，采用图文并茂、中英文结合的形式，力求达到学术性与艺术性的统一，满足各类读者的需求。

山东省文化和旅游厅领导始终关心本书的编撰与出版工作，并在编撰过程中给予了全力支持，在此表示诚挚谢意。

本书的编纂工作得到了山东省十六地市非遗保护中心及省直文化系统工作人员的大力帮助与支持，他们对本书定稿做了最后的校对工作；本书的英文翻译和出版工作由山东大学出版社完成，在此一并表示感谢。

本书文字资料来源于十六地市省级代表性传承人申报书，书中配图由十六地市非遗中心提供。由于编者水平所限，遗漏、缺憾之处在所难免，恳请读者谅解并给予指正。

The Representative Inheritors of the Provincial Intangible Cultural Heritage Projects of Shandong Province is a complete and systematic introduction to the representative inheritors of intangible cultural heritage projects in Shandong Province, and also an important tool book to promote intangible cultural heritage in Shandong Province. It records the basic information, technical characteristics, apprentice inheritance and other aspects of the representative inheritors of intangible cultural heritage projects in Shandong Province. It adopts the form of combination of pictures and texts, Chinese and English, and strives to achieve the unity of academic and artistic, to meet the needs of all kinds of readers.

Leaders of Shandong Provincial Department of culture and tourism have always been concerned about the compilation and publication of this book, and have given full support in the compilation process, and hereby express sincere thanks. The compilation of this book has been greatly helped and supported by the intangible cultural heritage protection center of sixteen cities in Shandong Province and the staff of the cultural system directly under the provincial government, who have made the final proofreading work for this book. The English translation and publication of this book were completed by Shandong University Press, thanks also here.

The text data of this book comes from the declaration of the provincial representative inheritors of sixteen cities, and the drawings in the book are provided by the intangible cultural heritage center of sixteen cities. Due to the limited level of editors, omissions and defects are inevitable, please understand and correct.

图书在版编目（CIP）数据

山东省省级非物质文化遗产项目代表性传承人．第三卷 / 李国琳主编．— 济南：山东大学出版社，2019.10
ISBN 978-7-5607-6503-7

Ⅰ．①山… Ⅱ．①李… Ⅲ．①非物质文化遗产—民间艺人—生平事迹—山东—现代 Ⅳ．①K825.7

中国版本图书馆 CIP 数据核字（2019）第 259877 号

责任编辑：张　瑞　王　潇
封面设计：牛　钧

出版发行：山东大学出版社
社　址　山东省济南市山大南路 20 号
邮　编　250100
电　话　市场部（0531）88363008
经　销：新华书店
印　刷：济南巨丰印刷有限公司
规　格：889 毫米 ×1194 毫米　1/16
10 印张　　256 千字
版　次：2019 年 10 月第 1 版
印　次：2019 年 10 月第 1 次印刷
定　价：260.00 元